CONCRETE BOATBUILDING

Concrete Boatbuilding

ITS TECHNIQUE AND ITS FUTURE

By

GAINOR W. JACKSON, JNR
W. MORLEY SUTHERLAND

Illustrated by GAINOR W. JACKSON, JNR

John de Graff, Inc
TUCKAHOE, NEW YORK

FIRST PUBLISHED IN 1969
SECOND IMPRESSION 1969
THIRD IMPRESSION 1971

BRITISH SBN 0 04 623005 X

U.S. SBN 8 286 0037–6
First published in U.S.A. 1969
John de Graff, Inc
34 Oak Avenue, Tuckahoe, N.Y., 10707

PRINTED IN GREAT BRITAIN

FOR DAVINA, JEREMY, AND HUGO JACKSON
AND
LEE, ROSS, PETER, AND ANNE SUTHERLAND

Foreword

BY DR PIER LUIGI NERVI

It was with much pleasure and satisfaction that I agreed to write the foreword to this book by Gainor Jackson and Morley Sutherland. At one time in my life I dedicated myself exclusively to reinforced concrete constructions, and I still consider this method of construction the most elegant that man has hitherto invented, and one whose possibilities of application are still far from exhausted.

Ferro-cement, one of the many possible versions of reinforced concrete, came into being towards the end of the Second World War. At this time the object was its employment in the field of naval construction. I myself was convinced that ferro-cement could contribute decisively to the reconstruction of light and medium shipping destroyed in the war, and I remember with great nostalgia the first experiments performed, the satisfaction with the results obtained, and the endless discussions necessary in order to acquire the necessary approval from the Italian Naval Register and premiums from the insurance companies comparable to those for wood or iron hulls.

Unfortunately, in the following years, my initial enthusiasm gradually waned as a direct result of the lack of interest that the application of ferro-cement received as a medium for naval constructions. As a consequence I abandoned my work in this field, though still remained absolutely convinced of the validity of the principles. Two of the major influences in my decision have been the rigid adherence to tradition of the navies of the world and my success in the employment of ferro-cement in other fields of construction.

I feel justifiably satisfied, therefore, when I see that others have understood the intrinsic qualities of ferro-cement and appreciate the graceful and interesting applications realized in recent years. The authors have been most flattering in describing my contribution in this field, and in my turn I thank them for having revived interest in the maritime applications of ferro-cement.

I am convinced today, as I was twenty-five years ago, that ferro-cement can find a wide and ever-multiplying place in the world of sailing, and in particular in the design and construction of fishing boats. This book is without doubt the best guide to concrete boats for all unprejudiced people interested in things of the sea.

Rome September 1968

Introduction

The very idea of building light, thin-walled boats of concrete usually amazes the average man. Most people have the impression that concrete is heavy, brittle, and easily cracked in tension. And it often does have all these drawbacks. It is equally true, since the development of ferro-cement after the last war, that concrete members can be light, astonishingly flexible and capable of resisting considerable impact without cracking.

Ferro-cement in the form we know it today was pioneered by the great Italian engineer, Dr Pier Luigi Nervi, assisted by others who worked with him. Nervi based his thinking on the observation that the elasticity of a reinforced concrete member increases in proportion to the subdivision and distribution of the reinforcement of the mass. After much practical and laboratory test work, it became clear that several layers of mesh reinforcing, in combination with steel rods embedded (but only thinly covered) in a rich mortar, produced a very strong resilient material. Dr Nervi gave it the name ferro-cemento.

A thin concrete plank made in this way could bend and spring back, without any apparent cracking, and in fact had in this respect the characteristics of Canadian Spruce. An ideal material, he reasoned, from which to build boats. It was clearly very strong and just as light as either steel or wood for boats over about forty feet. It was cheaper and an easier material with which to build. None of the usual framework associated with concrete was required. The material was fireproof to a remarkable degree, and capable of resisting high impacts.

When subjected to a blow that would completely open up an ordinary wooden hull, ferro-cement merely shattered in a localized way with the concrete retained sufficiently to resist the gross passage of water; obviously a great advantage, this, in boat construction. Moreover, it was a simple matter to repair such damage, and merely involved the tidying up of any damaged reinforcing and re-plastering the hole.

No longer would any of the tedious maintenance associated with wooden and steel hulls be necessary.

Dr Nervi proceeded with his work, and a company of which he was founder, Nervi and Bartoli, built several ferro-cement boats just after the 1939–45 War. All were highly successful. Unfortunately, Dr Nervi and his company soon became engaged in major constructional projects and lacked the time to proceed further in the field of boatbuilding. In a letter some months ago to the authors, Professor Nervi expresses regret that his realizations in ferro-cement boats have not been more numerous. It is understood, however, that he recently has been engaged by the Food and Agriculture Organization of the United Nations to advise on the construction of concrete fishing vessels. This organization has also sought advice from co-author W. M. Sutherland concerning New Zealand's widespread experience in this field.

Dr Nervi wrote a paper on the practical and theoretical aspects of ferro-cement in 1951, and also quoted some of the associated research of Professor Oberti. This paper has since become a standard reference in engineering circles.

Slowly, since its publication, the world has awakened to the great scope for boatbuilding inherent in the medium. In the last few years many other papers have appeared on aspects of the material and hundreds of ferro-cement boats have been built around the world. Interest in their unique qualities is quickening to an astonishing degree, and one can say, without hesitation, that a very significant revolution in boatbuilding has begun.

New Zealand, a small but prosperous country of 2·75 millions, has been in the van of the concrete boat revolution. Morely Sutherland and Arthur Manning, the two pioneers there, have seen their efforts greatly rewarded. In Auckland, Ferro-Cement Ltd, under the technical directorship of Mr Sutherland, have to their credit the widest range of concrete boats yet built anywhere in the world.

Britain has also been well to the fore in this development. Notable among the British pioneers in ferro-cement boatbuilding have been lawyer-businessman Thomas Hagenbach, and his nephew, Engineer Paul Hagenbach of Windboats Ltd, and Mr A. J. Harris, an eminent structural engineer of London. Windboats Ltd are building ferro-cement boats in a thoroughly commercial manner at their yards in Wroxham, Norfolk, and have a large number to their credit.

A small number of ferro-cement craft have been built also in the United States, and it is understood that the first commercial boat-yard recently began work there. But strangely, comparatively little has been done yet in this field in the USA except for floating marinas, and the door seems wide open there. Canada, Australia and South Africa all have a respectable roll of ferro-cement boats.

One cannot help noticing that so far the greatest development in this field has taken place in Britain, New Zealand and to a lesser extent the other main members of the British Commonwealth. An explanation may lie in the fact that Dr Nervi's paper was translated into English (from the Italian article which appeared in *L'Ingegnere*, 1951, No. 1) by the Cement and Concrete Association, London. From there its impact spread through the Commonwealth. Not much is known of recent developments in Russia, but several experimental glass cement boats were built there in 1961. Several ferro-cement boats have been built in Europe, but not as many as in the British Commonwealth.

There is, however, one notable exception to this tidy theory of how the idea has spread, although not an argument against it. The People's Republic of China could now be said to have more ferro-cement boats than all other countries combined. The Chinese freely admit their debt to New Zealand for the basic ideas which encouraged them to set up their astonishing sampan building factory.

At the Wusih plant, not far west of Shanghai, a staff of 600 (20 per cent of whom are women) are engaged in the production of six basic sampans, on a highly efficient production line. These range between 3-ton burden (28 feet) craft, to 5-ton (30 feet) models. Despite initial scepticism from conservative peasants, the builders soon proved their arguments. They loaded the sampans with heavy loads, raced them against wooden boats, rammed them into banks, and so on, to great effect. The additional advantages of greatly reduced cost (they cost one-third less than wooden sampans) and the fact that the raw materials are plentiful, whereas timber is scarce, won the day. Nor could these vessels be burnt if a charcoal brazier fell over, and they required much less maintenance than wooden sampans. Thousands now ply the great network of waterways feeding into China's Grand Canal.

Although thin walled ferro-cement boats have been widely accepted only in the last few years, thin concrete hulls, reinforced in a cruder way, are not new. It will astonish many readers to know that the oldest remaining examples of reinforced concrete in any form, are two rowing boats, still in existence after one hundred years and after having lain for more than half a century beneath the waters of Lake Miraval, in France. One is in perfect condition, and although the other shows that mistakes were made in layering the mortar, even this vessel is still capable of floating; a compelling answer surely to sceptics who fear that the reinforcing will rust through concrete boats. There are other examples of very old mortar boats, and now we also know about the performance of those ferro-cement boats built by Dr Nervi after the second war. It is now certain that the material has very high durability.

During the first war many concrete ships and barges were built. Later in the second world war, more sea-going ships, barges and the floating caissons and piers of Arromanches Harbour were built in conventional reinforced concrete. The concrete vessels of all kinds commissioned in Britain, the USA and Europe during both wars could well displace half a million tons. These vessels, generally speaking, proved very sound structurally despite their experimental nature.

The factor which stifled the further development of sea-going self-propelled ships in peacetime was their weight. Concrete hulls, reinforced in the old conventional manner, are normally heavier than steel hulls. The relatively greater power required to drive them made these ships uneconomic in competition with steel plate hulls. Many engineers, however, believe that concrete may still have a future in ship construction, but it is likely that future ships will be reinforced differently—possibly as the great French engineer and concrete shipbuilder, Eugene Freyssinet, suggested, by using high tensile steel under tension. 'Prestressing will enable us to build ships of such dimensions that the biggest waves will be only a choppy sea to them.'

No such weight disadvantage, however, arises in the field of *ferro-cement* boat-building, which can be used for vessels of, say, one hundred feet in length. Such boats (over say forty-five feet) are usually lighter than steel or wood. Hulls under this size, although of similar or marginally heavier weights than wood and steel, are often at no disadvantage since most displacement yachts have to be ballasted in any case. Heavier displacement power boats require slightly more energy to start in motion, but carry their way better than lighter boats. Weight is not usually a very important factor in small displacement hulls.

We have tried in this book to explain in detail the technique of building a ferro-cement boat; how the mortar should be mixed, the reinforcing armature constructed,

13

and the concrete plastered. Although care must be taken in building concrete boats, as indeed with any boat, the skills demanded of the amateur are perhaps less than required to build a comparable boat in wood. And on the whole, the work is physically easier. The cost of building larger pleasure craft in concrete is certainly less than in any competing material. On this ground alone, the technique promises to have a great impact on future small-boat building.

Although here and there we have touched on the theoretical aspects of ferro-cement, the book is intended to be a practical guide for the intending builder, as well as providing a background to the history and characteristics of concrete in boatbuilding. Boatbuilding in concrete, as in any other material, is a practical craft. On the whole it will be done better by skilled professionals, but it is within the range of the semi-skilled to turn out a good job. Within this framework we hope that our book will prove useful, and informative.

GAINOR W. JACKSON

Auckland, N.Z.   W. MORLEY SUTHERLAND

Acknowledgements

In gathering material for this book we have sought assistance from many people in many countries. Without exception our inquiries produced most encouraging responses. To all who have contributed their valuable time we offer grateful thanks.

We are particularly indebted to Dr Pier Nervi, not only because of his pioneering work which made the book possible, but for his warm encouragement.

Although opinions expressed in the book are our own, we have obtained valuable assistance from technical papers on aspects of ferro-cement. Notable among these were papers by L. D. G. Collen, J. G. Byrne, Professor Wright, Nathan Bavli, Dr Ori Ishai, and Professor James Romualdi. We must also acknowledge a considerable debt to Mrs Jean Haviland of USA whose contribution to the brief history of concrete ships has been invaluable. Also to the editor of *Concrete Products*, Chicago, for permission to publish the photos of sampan building in the Peoples Republic of China.

All the following have made valuable contributions, and we regret that space restricts us from expressing our thanks more fully: N. Rodokal, Ray Natali, and R. L. Stewart, N.Z. yacht designer, who have been extremely helpful; Douglas Alexander, who gave much assistance in the section on commercial fishing vessels; Donald and Paul Hagenbach of Windboats Ltd, England; A. J. Harris, Michael Gage, and R. Elkington, all also of England; Brian Wilson; A. A. Van Der Vlist, editor of *Cement* Magazine, Amsterdam; G. Worontzoff of the Societe Technique Pour L'Utilization de la Precontrainte, Paris; R. Knapp of Bauverlag G. m.b.h. Berlin; Martin Iorns of Sacremento; John Mallitte of *Seaspray* Magazine, N.Z. We are also indebted to Noel Holmes, Gifford Jackson, Margaret Mason, Pat Sweet, Mrs P. Adler, Gainor Jackson snr., who translated several French papers, and Michael Felgate-Catt for his practical encouragement. Also Arthur Manning, who enjoys the distinction of being the first man to build a ferro-cement boat in New Zealand.

To our wives Elizabeth and Hazel, who have suffered so much, uncomplainingly, we owe more than we can express.

Contents

B

Plates

CHAPTER 1

The slow development of cement and concrete

The discovery that burnt lime mixed with water made a crude cement was made a very long time ago. Like the discovery of plastics in recent times, it was probably accidental. One intriguing theory of its origin suggests that a primitive man, using limestone as a fireplace, found that the burnt rocks surrounding the fire disintegrated into a white paste following hard rain. Later, when the sun came out, it was discovered that this putty-like material had hardened. One can imagine that it would not have been long before such a useful material was put to work as a filling for cracks in walls, and possibly boats, as well as to take up irregularities between building blocks. It is known that the Chinese long ago used burnt lime to build boats, in combination with a reinforcement of bamboo rods.

Such a crude lime cement was certainly used as far back as 3000 BC and possibly earlier. Burnt gypsum was used later as a mortar, when the pyramids of Gizeh (the largest of which is 450 feet high) were built. It has been suggested that the wet lime may have been thought of as a lubricant to move the blocks, but this seems hardly likely, since the mortar would dry easily in the sun and in any case better lubricants would have been available. It does not seem to have been long before knowledge of this material spread around the Mediterranean. Pliny the Elder, that learned and very curious Roman historian, who perished in AD 79 while investigating the eruption of Mount Vesuvius, records that the Greek Palace of Croesus (*circa* 550 BC) was covered with a rendering in which burnt lime was used. Lime is found so universally around the world that it is perhaps not surprising that other peoples outside the Mediterranean area stumbled across its use as cement, apparently quite independently of one another. The Mogul Indians, Mayas, Incas and Chinese, all used it early in their history.

It is, however, to those great builders and engineers, the Romans, that we must look for the first general use of burnt lime with aggregate to make concrete. The early history of cement and concrete are, of course, inextricably interwoven, but the Romans seem to have been the first people really to have understood the significance of concrete as a structural material rather than merely as a mortar. Their development of a strong concrete from the early crude mortars was not, however, achieved overnight. The great improvement which made hard setting cement possible was the addition to the lime of pozzolana, a crushed red volcanic powder which slowly combined with the lime. This combination produced a material far stronger and harder than had been possible before. Although examples of broken stone aggregate with a lime and sand mortar can be seen in remains at Pompeii, built about 300 BC, pozzolana concrete does not seem to have been employed for a further 300 years. But by the first century AD, it was being used increasingly and intelligently in major building projects, several of which remain in astonishingly good condition today.

The earliest known example of the addition of pozzolana to lime dates back to 55 BC, when the combination was used in the construction of the theatre at Pompeii. The qualities of the new material were quickly appreciated, and many notable buildings were built with its aid over the next hundred years.

That great architect and engineer, the Emperor Hadrian, was one who used concrete intelligently and in bold and fresh ways. He seems to have understood the material very well and frequently supervised construction work himself. In England

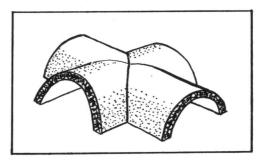

Fig. 1.—The Romans were the first to discover that relatively thin shells of concrete could take considerable loads in compression.

in AD 122 he personally surveyed the line of Hadrian's Wall by walking on foot the entire 73½ miles—'hatless in all weathers' it has been recorded. The concrete abutments of the bridge carrying this wall over the North Tyne river can be seen to this day. But Hadrian's crowning achievement in concrete was surely the noble dome of the Pantheon in Rome. Even now, nearly two thousand years later, the great dome is still the largest of its type in the world, with a span of 43·3 metres, exceeding even that of St Peter's (42·52 metres). Built originally as a temple to all gods it is now a Christian church, and the best preserved and finest example of Roman architecture remaining. Hadrian's conception of the way concrete should be used in the dome was to be taken up again and again by later architects. The base of this huge dome is very thick and contains a strong concrete of crushed brick and stone. The dome walls then thin away gradually towards the crown, and even the concrete itself changes to a light-weight pumice aggregate.

The Romans built better than they knew, and hundreds of examples of their use of concrete in walls, aqueducts, breakwaters and foundations scattered throughout

Europe, still remain in excellent preservation. Because they did not have suitable mixing and crushing machines, the material was still often thought of as a mortar. The mix frequently was poured over packed stones and the structure built up layer by layer with or without the use of wooden formwork. Usually, the Romans used a mix of five parts of pozzolana to two parts of lime, and it is clear from early records that they knew the importance of curing. In their instructions for repairs to aqueducts, for example, it was laid down that work should be executed between April and November, but not on hot summer days.

With the passing of the Roman Empire went much of the accumulated knowledge of concrete. Later, the Normans began to use it again, but on the whole their mortars were merely of sand and lime, although they did sometimes add crushed bricks which would have had an action somewhat akin to that of pozzolana. They tended to use the mix as mortar in conjunction with stone blocks such as in their great castles of Richmond and Pevensey. As R. M. Titford points out in *The Golden Age of Concrete*, edited by him for the great Danish construction company, Christiani and Nielsen Ltd, 'No further advance in the use of concrete appears to have been made in the following 500 years, by which time the French had just about caught up with where the Romans left off 500 years before'. By 1568, Philibert de L'Orme, a French architect, could write:

'The best and surest method is to prepare a mortar composed of quicklime recently burnt, mixed with river sand which contains a quantity of pebbles of all sizes, provided the largest is not bigger than the fist or the size of an egg, and that the whole be interspersed with smaller pebbles and gravel, such as is usually found in rivers. This material, moistened with water and mingled with lime serves both for mortar and stone, and mixed with sufficient quantity of sand must be thrown at once into the excavation without any labour from the mason's trowel.'

This marks the earliest recorded specification for graded aggregates, one of the great milestones in the development of concrete.

Later, de L'Orme explains that,

'the composition thus executed hardens and solidifies so firmly in the foundations that, being heaped up in a mass and bound together, it becomes a uniform body or rock, such as nature forms, of a single block and so strong and hard that when dry it cannot be broken either by piles or any other instrument, nor can the pebbles be separated from it without breaking them to pieces'.

Concrete as a strong plastic building material was beginning to be better understood.

By the eighteenth century interest had begun to quicken in the chemistry of concrete and much experimenting into the nature of cement was taking place. The great engineer, John Smeaton, who used concrete at the base of the third Eddystone Lighthouse, built in 1756, was a key figure. He wrote in his papers that his cement 'would equal the best merchantable Portland stone in solidarity and durability'.

It is from his association of cement with Portland stone that he is sometimes, although wrongly, regarded as the father of Portland cement, a development which was to come about seventy years later.

When Smeaton began work on the third Eddystone Lighthouse, he realized the vital importance of strong foundations. Fifty-three years before, the first lighthouse built of wood and fastened to the rock with iron bars had been swept away, with its designer, in a great storm. The second tower, also built of wood, had burned down. Smeaton had the job of anchoring his new lighthouse to a rock which was exposed only at low tide, and without the aid of cement mixing machines and mechanical drills! The use of his new concrete in laying the foundation courses for the stone tower is a great milestone in concrete development. When one takes into account the fact that only about two hours a day were available before the sea began breaking over the work, makes the achievement even more notable. How successful he was is still evident, for although the ravages of the sea eventually undermined the rock on which the light was built, the foundations remained firm. When the present fourth light was built, Smeaton's tower was dismantled and rebuilt at Plymouth Hoe, but the foundations and the first floor still remain, a solemn monument to the great engineer.

Other notable figures arose during the eighteenth century, such as D. Saussune, and James Parker of Kent. Parker introduced what was known as 'Roman' cement, and he took out a patent for this in 1796. Parker was the first to appreciate the value of high temperature burning. Several other British pioneers such as Frost, Pasley, and White played their part, but it was not until a Leeds' bricklayer, Joseph Aspdin, patented a new process which he called Portland Cement, in 1824, that the development of cement as we know it began. He did not perfect the process, but others were soon able to stand on his shoulders. One was an experimenter called Johnson, who found that by grinding some of the hard clinker and gauging it with water, a much stronger although slower setting cement resulted. Johnson wrote of his experiments these historical words:

'I pulverized some of the clinker and gauged it. It did not seem as though it would harden at all and no warmth was produced. I then made mixtures of the powdered clinker and powdered lightly-burned stuff and this did set and soon became hard. On examination some days later of the clinker only, I found it was much harder than this material; moreover, the colour was a nice grey.'

The concrete revolution we are witnessing could be said then to have started.

Great improvements in processes, kilns and mixers followed rapidly during the next hundred years. As far back as 1877 an association was set up in Germany to improve the quality of cement, and its strength has improved dramatically as a result of scientific enquiry. The graph shows how greatly cement strength has increased after its long slow beginning. The figures, apart from the latest one, are based on a paper read by Professor A. W. Skempton in 1962, at the London Science Museum. Professor Skempton has related the various cements to a common basis to make the comparison possible. One can hardly fail to feel excited about the future of the material, if this speeded rate of developments can be maintained.

Primitive cements were made from hydrated lime and mixed with sand to make mortar. Hydrated lime, when mixed to a paste with water and sand, gradually hardens as a result partly of drying out, and partly of a reaction with atmospheric carbon dioxide. The sand takes no part in the reaction. The development of strength is slow and uneven, and the paste does not harden at all if immersed in water.

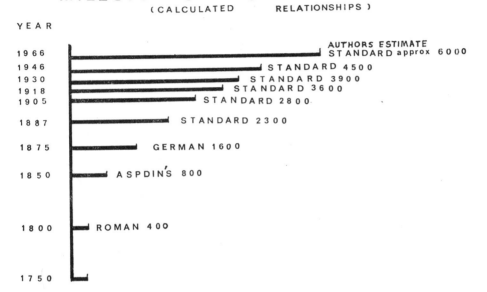

MILESTONES IN CEMENT DEVELOPMENT

(CALCULATED   RELATIONSHIPS)

COMPRESSION STRENGTHS : LBS PER SQUARE INCH

Fig. 2

Modern hydraulic cements, however, such as Portland cement, set hard when mixed into a paste with water, not through drying out, but from chemical reactions between the water and compounds present. These reactions occur not only if the paste is left to stand in air but also if it is placed in water. Unlike the old cements, the improved products are of low permeability to water, and nearly insoluble in water.

So cement has slowly evolved over thousands of years, and with it the development of strong concrete. That concrete was a remarkable plastic material which, when set, had great resistance to compression, was no longer in doubt. But it was not until the middle of the nineteenth century that a French farmer, Joseph Louis Lambot, thought of the idea of combining iron with concrete to give added tensile

25

strength and to increase vastly its use as a building material. Now it was capable of resisting tension as well as compression. The Romans, nearly two thousand years before, had used iron and bronze ties outside concrete to increase its strength and this technique had persisted ever since, but to use iron *within* concrete was a great stride forward. *It will fascinate readers of this book to learn that one of the very first applications of ferro-concrete was in the construction by Lambot of a concrete boat in 1848 to float on the lake at the bottom of his garden at Miraval* in France. It was constructed to demonstrate Lambot's idea of substituting for wood, a combination of iron mesh and cement. Thus reinforced concrete was born, and with its discovery the beginning of the great revolution in construction, which over the last sixty or seventy years has so transformed the face of the earth.

As our book develops, we will look closely at the development of a new form of reinforced concrete called ferro-cement, and how this strong, flexible and elastic material can be used to great advantage in small-boat building.

CHAPTER 2

The background of ferro-cement

Ferro-cement, as the name suggests, is reinforced mortar. It is the particular way it is reinforced with a combination of wire mesh and steel rods that makes the material unique. Although ferro-cement as we now know it, was not really understood until toward the end of the last war, when Professor Pier Luigi Nervi of Italy began testing his own theories, ferro-cement in a crude form is as old as reinforced concrete itself.

Reinforced concrete, one of man's most important discoveries, began as described in Miraval, France. There on his farm, Joseph Louis Lambot made the worlds first reinforced concrete products early in the 1840s. It seems strange that it should have taken man so long to develop the theory of ferro-cement, when the very first use of reinforced concrete at all, took the form of mesh reinforced mortar. Yet it took nearly a hundred years from its first beginnings, until Dr Nervi and other Italian collaborators fully developed the material as we know it. It is also rather curious that it has taken nearly twenty years for knowledge of the enormous potential of Dr Nervi's pioneering work to spread. There is, it would seem, an inevitable time lag between fundamental research and its widespread practical application.

Joseph Lambot's contribution

Lambot was born in 1814 in Mountfort, the son of a Provençal aristocrat. He was given a good basic education at Aix, the capital of Provence, and later studied in Paris. Before finally settling at Miraval, he travelled widely, and it is likely that this stimulus greatly enriched his very curious mind, for one invention followed another during the remainder of his life. There is evidence that his opinions were highly regarded by many during his time.

Provence is a rather dry area, and building timber has always been at a premium there. It may have been this that led Lambot to experiment by reinforcing mortar to make articles for which he might normally have used wood. It is certainly clear from the explanation to his patents for *ferciment* in 1855, that he thought of the invention as a substitute for wood. Lambot's historical patents gave him protection in England and Belgium. The description to the patents reads:

'My invention shows a new product which helps to replace timber where it is endangered by wetness, as in wood flooring, water containers, plant pots, etc. The new substance consists of a metal net of wire or sticks which are connected or formed like a flexible woven mat.

'I give this net a form which looks in the best possible way, similar to the article I want to create. Then I put in hydraulic cement or similar bitumin tar or mix, to fill up the joints.'

Plate 1 shows metal reinforcing which can be used in a water container as well as in a plant tub.
   A. Durable net.
   B. Bedded in cement.
   C. Metal stability. Bar (or stick).
   D. Iron net.
Figure 2 shows the interior build-up of reinforcing which can be used in place of a wooden floor cover or beam.
   A. Plate on which metal rods are fastened.
   B. Frame for bedding the rods.
   C. Material bedded in.
   D. Metal rods.
   E. Rivets.

'These are the applications which can be modified if required. For example, in the construction of a beam 25×25 cm., one chooses an iron wire of 7 mm.

'For the duration of my patent I, as the spiritual owner of the wood-substitute product, take the right to use it solely for my own benefit.'

Before Lambot applied for his patents he had already made plant tubs, water tanks and none other than a concrete rowing boat for the lake at the foot of his property! This was exhibited at the Paris World Fair in 1855, catalogue number 4094.

Two of Lambot's friends, an engineer called Guerin, and a retired sea Captain Tanaran, were so convinced of the value of Lambot's invention that they signed a declaration that it was suitable to replace many types of wood construction both over the water, and under, which would otherwise rot.

During the years following the historical patent, Lambot constructed many more boats which eye witnesses enthused over. Several seem to have been launched on the little mountain river Argens, but unfortunately, not much is known of their history.

Although Lambot's system of using a single mesh reinforcement for mortar would not have the same characteristics as modern ferro-cement, it has stood the test of time. Both Lambot's original two rowing boats are still in existence (Plate 2d) today, more than a hundred years after being launched, and after half a century buried under mud beneath the Miraval Lake. One boat is in excellent condition, and the other, although in remarkably good shape, shows evidence that Lambot made a mistake in attempting to bond different layers of mortar together. This faulty boat may have been the first he built, and if so, it is the oldest reinforced concrete product of any kind existing in the world. But the one in better condition may have been even older, for the reason we shall mention shortly.

Had it not been for a Marseilles builder, M Gassier de Bastide, who noticed one of these boats by chance in 1902 while strolling on the Lambot property (Lambot had long since died), both boats might have been lost for ever. A photograph taken at this time clearly shows the now faulty boat floating on the lake (Plate 3*b*). One wonders whether the boat now in better condition may have been older and already at the bottom of the lake.

Fortunately de Bastide soon afterwards published an article on his findings at the farm, in the house Journal *Le béton armé* of the French firm Hennebique. In 1950, when thoughts of celebrating the hundredth anniversary of the birth of reinforced concrete arose, someone remembered this article and a team was raised to search the pond at Miraval. At first the party was unsuccessful, but later in 1955 when the water level was very low, they succeeded in tearing the boats from the reeds and mud. The so-called older boat (the one now in faulty condition) was exhibited at Paris that year, and given publicity in the magazine *Béton*.

This boat at least is now at Brignoles, where it can be inspected at the local museum. The whereabouts of the other boat is not known to us at the time of writing. From photos it seems clear that even the deteriorated shell would still float, and the boat in better condition looks as good as new.

No words could give a better testimonial of the strength and durability of the closely reinforced rich mortar of Lambot's two boats. Even though the cement was poor by modern standards, and the system of reinforcing less sophisticated than that currently used, the concrete has lasted magnificently, and would seem to be almost indestructible in normal use: a wonderful answer for the sceptics of today who fear the reinforcing in ferro-cement boats will rust away.

Lambot attributed most of the same qualities to his 'ferciment' as did Professor Nervi to his more sophisticated product ferro-cement; named incidentally quite independently of Lambot. Before Lambot applied for a patent in 1855 he claims in a booklet that this new material is:

1. Non-inflammable.
2. Cheap to use.
3. Requires no upkeep.
4. Quick to build in.
5. Easily repaired in the event of damage.
6. Chemically stable.
7. Impervious to water.

Lambot was, of course, not the only great early pioneer of reinforced concrete. Other great figures such as Monier, Coignet, Hennebique, Hyatt, and Wilkinson, all made important contributions. But Lambot it seems was the very first, and because he devised a technique of cement boatbuilding so fundamentally similar to that now beginning to be widely used around the world, he is of special interest to us here.

29

Dr Nervi's Contribution

Dr Pier Luigi Nervi was born on June 21, 1891, at Sondrio. In his long life he has had a very considerable influence on the use of concrete in many fields, and he will go down in the history of architecture as a great artist as well as engineer. He has at all times been passionately devoted to the detailing and calculation of the elements within a structure. This quality, the painstaking engineer in him, combined with his great aesthetic sensitivity and boldness, has given the world many of its most breathtakingly beautiful structures.

Today in Rome Dr Nervi with his two sons directs a study centre for concrete construction. Dr Nervi is also head of his own construction firm, Nervi and Bartoli.

In 1943, nearly a hundred years after Lambot's patent, Dr Nervi began experimenting on an original concept of reinforcing cement mortar with *superimposed* layers of wire mesh and small diameter bars. He based his thinking on the observation that the elasticity of a reinforced concrete member increases in proportion to the subdivision and distribution of the reinforcement throughout the mass.

We could not do better than quote from *L'Ingegnere* 1951, No. 1, a translation of Dr Nervi's own words:

'Starting from this point I wondered what would be the behaviour of a slab made by clothing in cement mortar a number of layers of wire tied together with wire. The wires were from 0·02″ to 0·06″ diameter, with a 0·4″ square mesh (approximately $\frac{4}{10}$ inch) and a weight varying between 0·14 lb. and 0·35 lb. per square foot, of the type normally used in the construction of ceilings, or in making concrete products.

'The mortar was made of good quality sand, in proportions varying from one cubic foot of sand to 60–75 lb. of cement.

'In this way very thin slabs were made which were exceptionally flexible and elastic as well as extremely strong.'

'To increase the thickness and strength of the slabs without using more than ten to twelve layers of mesh, I subsequently tried introducing between the layers of mesh, one or more layers of bars of a diameter of $\frac{1}{4}$ to $\frac{3}{4}$ inch, and was able in this way to obtain thicknesses of from 2·3 inches to 3·9 inches without losing any of the qualities of the material formed with the mesh alone.'

'In every case the thickness of the finished slab was only a very little greater than that of the assembled layers of mesh, the difference being only sufficient to provide adequate cover for the steel.'

Nervi soon found that thin slabs of cement mortar reinforced in this way behaved quite differently from ordinary reinforced concrete. They were flexible to an astonishing degree, and had the mechanical characteristics of a completely homogeneous material. For example, a plank made of ferro-cement could be supported at both ends, and when weighted in the middle it would bend rather like wood. When eventually unweighted it would again resume its old shape.

Clearly a new material had been discovered which confounded much 'common-sense' thinking on the nature of concrete. Apart from such surprising flexibility and elasticity, the material proved to be exceptionally strong, and capable of resisting high impact.

These qualities, and the fact that the ferro-cement was so much lighter than normal reinforced concrete, led Dr Nervi to the conclusion that it would have considerable application in naval work, for building small ships.

In the summer of 1943, before the end of the war, the Italian Naval Register supervised further tests in a yard belonging to the firm Nervi and Bartoli at Torre del Lago (Viareggio). Later, in Rome, at the Laboratory of the Experimental Institute for Building Construction, yet further tests were carried out under the direction of Professor Martinelli. The results of these tests confirmed Nervi's views. Both the Naval Register, and the Department of Marine Engineering of the Italian Navy, accepted the new material and it was decided to order three 150-ton motor vessels for the Navy. All were to have ferro-cement hulls.

As well as these, a larger vessel of 400 tons was ordered at the same time. The frame of this vessel was built up of precast reinforced concrete, and the skin was made of wood planking. The hulls of the smaller vessels were to be of ferro-cement.

By this time the military situation in Italy made it impossible to procede further, and the firm Nervi and Bartoli, who were building the vessels at Pelestrina (Venezia), had to abandon the projects.

Although doubtless a bitter disappointment to Dr Nervi, this was not to be the end of his attempts to put the material to marine use. Two years later, in the summer of 1945, the war then over, the firm Nervi and Bartoli built for its own use a 165-ton motor yacht *Irene* in the yard of Lazzarini and Meacci at Anzio. The construction of this ship demonstrated the simplicity of the technique, over traditional steel or wood. No formwork at all was required, the mortar being applied by hand to the mesh. Actually, as things were at the shipyard after the war, it would not have been easy to build in any other material, since no mechanical equipment remained, and no electricity was connected. One cannot imagine a vessel of this size being built in steel or wood under such conditions, in the three months it took to complete *Irene*.

The hull of the vessel was only 1·37 inches thick, and the total weight has been estimated to be 5 per cent less than the same vessel in wood. Its cost was thought to be about 40 per cent less than wood, and the price advantage over steel would have been even greater.

The reinforcing was built up from three layers of ¼ inch diameter bars at about 4 inch centres. Two of these ran longitudinally, and the other sandwiched in between ran transversely. Four layers of mesh were arranged on the inside of these bars and four on the outside. All eight were tightly tied with wire to the bars.

Dr Nervi reports in a paper written in 1951 that 'after five years of hard and regular use in the Mediterranean, the boat is as good as the day it was launched and has never required any maintenance whatever'.

He also records that the vessel had suffered two fairly serious accidents while sailing. On one occasion she ran aground in 1947, and a year later struck a wreck at Leghorn. Apart from some restricted damage at the point of impact, she was not holed in the normal sense and by using a simple hand pump it was possible to continue the voyage. About ten years ago *Irene* sank when blown in a storm onto the rocks of Sardinia.

Fig. 3.—*Irene*.

The earlier collisions before she sank were a practical confirmation of several shock tests which had been carried out by Professor Martinelli in 1943, on behalf of the Italian Naval Register. In Dr Nervi's own words:

'The shock-resistance experiment revealed not only the high strength of slabs only one inch thick (the tests were made by dropping a 5 cwt. weight on to samples 4 feet 6 inches square, from different heights, increasing to approximately 9 ft.) but also the fact that failure, when it occurred, did not consist of an actual hole in the structure, but rather a weakening of the wire mesh and a relatively dispersed breaking away of the mortar, the pieces of which still retained a certain cohesion, and a certain resistance to the passage of water. An obviously important point, this, in naval work.'

Later in 1947 Professor Oberti began tests at the Polytechnic Laboratory in Milan, to establish the degree of extension possible with ferro-cement samples

32

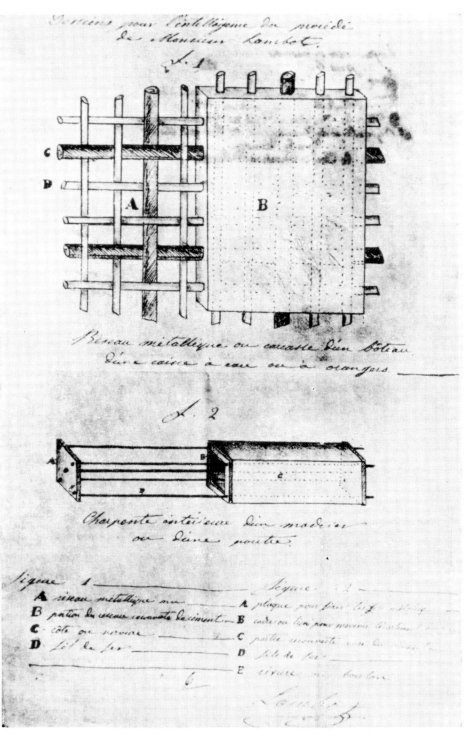

1 Facsimile of the world's first patent for reinforced concrete. Joseph Lambot who took it out called his product 'Ferciment'.

2*a* Cement testing, 1850.

b The Portland cement works of Aspdin
Ord & Co. at Gateshead-on-Tyne
(*circa* 1850).

c Joseph Louis Lambot.

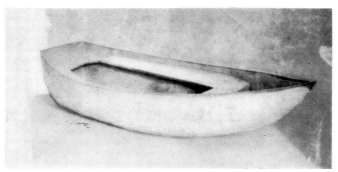

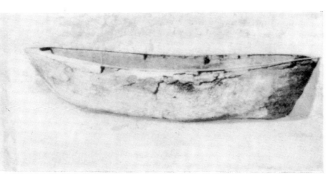

d The first ferro-concrete boat
the world. Built by Lambot
circa 1848, they were reclaim
from the bottom of a pond
in Southern France.

Photo taken in 1902 shows one of Lambot's boats on the pond of his former farm.

Nenelle, the world's first ferro-cement yacht is still in sound condition twenty years after being built, although not now used as a yacht.

c　Dr Pier Luigi Nervi

Photo: Courtesy of Dr. Nervi

Photo: W. T. U. Studios

4*a* Interior of 42-foot houseboat hull, looking forward. Made in sections and stressed together, by Windboats Ltd, Wroxham, Norfolk, UK. Because of the flatness of the sections stiffeners usually unnecessary in a curved hull, have been used.

b A 42-foot houseboat or barge hull built in 'Seacrete' by Windboats Ltd, Norfolk. This hull was manufactured in sections and subsequently assembled and stressed.

Photo: W. T. U. Studios

a *Falcon*, a ferro-cement ketch at the start of the Auckland to Suva yacht race. The day after, a bad storm blew up and one yacht sank; *Falcon* suffered no damage.

b *Veranima*, a 61-foot 38-ton displacement staysail schooner built in New Zealand by Mr Ferranti Chandos, in which he and his family intend to sail round the world. The bare hull and deck are reported to have cost only N.Z. $1,000 (£500 sterling).

Photo: Paul Farge

6 Seagull's eye view of Auckland yacht *Falcon* showing concrete deck and wood cabins.

7a Small wonder that ferro-cement sampans have been well received. Their cost is one third less than that of scarce timber. Bent oar known as a Yuloh is used as a sweep.

Photo: courtesy of Concrete Products, Chicago

b A 28-foot ferro-cement mission boat now in use in the New Hebrides Islands, under tow to another ferro-cement boat. The price of the finished vessel was much less than could be obtained in wood or steel. Built by Ferro Cement Ltd, New Zealand.

8a A 26-foot light displacement launch
built by Ferro-Cement Ltd on display
at Aucklands Boat Show.

 b A roomy 28-foot launch built by
Ferro-Cement Ltd.

 c *Arowhenua*, a privately built concrete
chine launch at Whangrarei, North
Auckland.

before visible cracking occurred. It was discovered that the percentage of steel in relation to the concrete mass was all important in reducing cracking.

When the layers of mesh and steel gave a ratio of from $5\frac{1}{2}$lb. to $11\frac{1}{2}$ lb. per cu. ft., the extensibility remained little better than that of unreinforced mortar. As the weight of steel increased however, about 27 lb. to 37 lb. per cu. ft., extensibility ratings improved to over five times more than before.

In practice it was found that when the cover of rich mortar was just sufficient to protect the layers of mesh and steel (in close contact with each other) then the weight of steel automatically reached a satisfactory weight in relation to the mass. This,

Fig. 4—A ferro-cement fishing vessel built by the firm Nervi & Bartoli after the last war.

C

as Dr Nervi points out, is the *natural* proportion for the material. When the thickness of the slab is increased in relation to the weight of steel, extensibility is lowered. Again it would be lowered by spacing out the mesh more thinly throughout the mass.

In passing, it could be noted that from a strength standpoint one can successfully build small boats thinner than the conventional ¾-inch thickness which is common nowadays on boats from, say, twenty-five feet to fifty feet. This thickness is used, however, to give the hull the necessary rigidity. Thinner skins than this tend to be too flexible when used on hulls of the above dimensions unless stiffeners are designed into the boat.

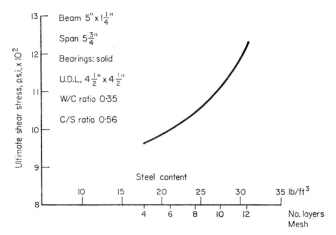

Fig. 5—Graph showing shear stress in relation to steel content where the latter varies from 17 lbs. to 32 lbs. of steel per cubic foot.

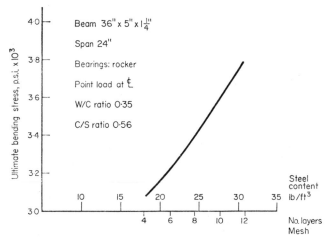

Fig. 6—Graph showing bending stress in relation to steel content where the latter varies from 17 lbs. to 32 lbs. of steel per cubic foot.

The firm of Nervi and Bartoli built other ferro-cement boats in the late forties—a fishing boat, the *San Rita*, and a yawl, *Nenelle*. *Nenelle* is still in sound condition more than twenty years after being built, despite rough handling. The fate of the *San Rita* is unknown.

Constructional techniques pioneered by the firm during this period have not altered very much since, and the contribution of Dr Nervi and his collaborators to the present revolution, has been immeasurable.

Fig. 7.—Test showing remarkable elasticity and flexibility of ferro-cement plank.

Let us look now at some experiments conducted by L. D. G. Collen of Eire on ferro-cement made basically in the same way as recommended by Dr Nervi.

The programme Mr Collen devised was to establish the bending strength, shear strength, and the modulus of elasticity of ferro-cement beams. The beams, size 3 feet × 5 inches wide × $1\frac{1}{4}$ inches deep (supported on rocker bearings and loaded centrally) were tested on a Buckton testing machine in the Engineering School of Trinity College.

The mesh used was a machine-woven non-galvanized mesh, 18 S.W.C. mild steel twin wires in the warp and a single wire in the weft. The mesh weighed 1·4 lb. per sq. yd. This unusual form, with twin wires in the warp, was necessary to make the fabric stable enough to withstand handling without resorting to welding or tying. Quarter inch mild steel bars were used at 3 inch centres with the mesh laid on each side. As Dr Nervi had observed, there was found to be a direct relationship between

35

the ultimate bending stress and the steel content. So also with shear test. The graphs (Figs. 5 and 6) published by Mr Collen are reproduced here with his kind permission.

A graphic impression of the strength, flexibility, and general characteristics of the material can be gained by comparing the values for the mechanical properties of Canadian spruce and ferro-cement, as set out below.

	Ferro-cement	Canadian Spruce
Young's modulus	820,000 to 1,300,000	750,000 to 1,200,000
Bending working stress	1,000 to 1,200	800 lb. per sq. in.
Shear working stress	100 to 400	100 lb. per sq. in.

CHAPTER 3

Other methods of reinforcing boats

Until now we have looked at only one method of reinforcing concrete boats; that is, by using several layers of small diameter light gauge steel mesh in combination with steel rods. This tried and tested technique has proved very satisfactory. There have been, however, interesting experiments in other forms of reinforcing in recent years, some of which may hold promise for the future. Let us look at some of these.

Expanded metal

Perhaps the most obvious variation of the current technique of reinforcing ferro-cement is to substitute expanded metal for the usually used square or hexagonal chicken wire. Expanded metal has some relative disadvantages, but it also has two great advantages. The first is that it is almost everywhere cheaper than welded or twisted mesh; the second, that because of its greater thickness (the mesh connections are twisted sideways) fewer layers are required to achieve a given thickness.

Some interesting research work has been done to evaluate the properties of expanded metal reinforcing by three men in Dublin, Mr Lyall D. G. Collen, Professor Wright and J. G. Byrne, and their observations are briefly summar zed here with their kind permission.

As Mr Collen points out, the fineness of the normally used wire mesh necessarily involves a high labour cost per lb. of finished steel which forces the price of the woven mesh up to about two and a half times the price of mild steel reinforcement. Normal fine woven mesh costs, in Eire, about 1s per lb., and the relative cheapness of expanded metal at 1s 1d per lb. gave hope that substantial savings could be expected, provided it was suitable in other respects.

Mr Collen conducted bending tests on a series of slabs, made up of non-vibrated mortar, mixed to a water/cement ratio of 0·35 and a cement/sand ratio of 0·56. The slabs were made up of two, four, and six layers of expanded metal, with ¼-inch diameter bars of mild steel sandwiched in the middle. The accompanying graphs illustrate the results of these tests. The first shows that, weight for weight, expanded metal is not quite as strong as woven fine wire mesh in *bending strength*. Cost for cost in Eire, at least, expanded metal has considerable advantages as the graph on relative costs shows.

Mr Collen makes the point that expanded metal is not as easily formed into

37

complex shapes as woven meshes, but the expanded metal being heavier, requires less labour per yard super. The tensible strength of the wire used in the woven mesh was 24 tons per square inch, and the sheet metal from which the expanded metal was manufactured had a similar strength.

J. G. Byrne and W. Wright, in their paper 'An Investigation of "Ferro-cement" using Expanded Metal' make some interesting points. 'There are', they say, 'no disadvantages in the use of expanded metal, and some advantages.'

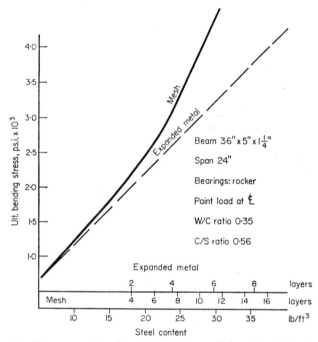

Fig. 8—The relative bending strengths of woven and expanded meshes. The latter is not as strong, weight for weight, in this regard.

They noted that during a tensile test with $\frac{1}{2}$ inch expanded-metal mesh weighing 4·77 lb. per square yard, the mortar split badly due to a scissors action of the diamond mesh, thus indicating that there is a limit to the size and weight of mesh. A $\frac{3}{8}$ inch mesh weighing 1·67 lb. per square yard and a 1 inch mesh up to 2·5 lb. per square yard proved satisfactory.

From a boatbuilding point of view, one would want to be very sure that the mesh was capable of being formed to the desired curves, othersise unsightly flat sections might result.

Aluminium

Aluminium, one might think. could hold certain advantages in reinforcing concrete, the most obvious, of course, being its lightness. Unfortunately, aluminium corrodes

38

in contact with wet cement and forms an aluminous salt which could spoil the bond. Perhaps this drawback could be overcome with a suitable coating on the aluminium.

There is, however, another problem. Aluminium expands about three times more than concrete per degree rise in temperature, whereas steel and concrete both have a similar co-efficient of expansion and contraction. Nor does it resist tension as well as high tensile steel.

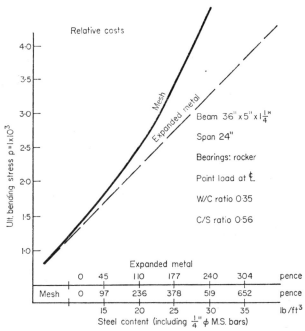

Fig. 9—Relative bending stresses of woven and expanded meshes. Here, expanded metal is shown to have an advantage in bending stress.

Glass-cement

A series of experiments with a material called glass-cement have recently been made in the USSR. Glass-cement is a laminated ansiomatic material comprising glass mesh and hardened cement paste. The strands of glass, which, incidentally, gain their great strength from surface tension, are protected from surface damage likely to arise from the setting cement paste by chemically stable polymers.

The June 1961 issue of *Beton i Zhelezobeton* contains many interesting details of the USSR experiments which, as far as we know, are not yet being widely applied in practice, but they seem to hold out exciting prospects for the future, although cost may weigh somewhat against it. One great advantage of this technique may be a weight reduction of between 55–65 per cent over steel reinforced concrete of equal strength.

The strength, elasticity and weight of the material are controlled by the cement/glass ratio, the cement past (made either with water or latex emulsion), the quality of the cement, the diameter of the glass filaments, and polymerization.

Two boats at least are known to have been built for experimental purposes, and they were highly satisfactory under test. As a result of the tests, two factories at Kiev have begun production of concrete boats.

Wirand

A new type of reinforced concrete which eliminates the need for the more conventional reinforcement of bars or mesh has been recently developed, called Wirand. In this material, short lengths of fine wire are mixed directly with the concrete in the mixer. These slivers of thin steel become embedded in the concrete closely spaced, and laying in random direction. If stainless steel wire could be used, this should overcome corrosion problems.

Wirand is said to be remarkably resistant to cracking and can resist high tensile stresses. One of its major advantages is that it can be cast into thin sections, less than one half an inch thick, and into any shape desired. Experimental work on Wirand is not yet regarded as complete.

For boatbuilding where moulds can be used, this technique, patented by the Batelle Memorial Institute, may have a considerable future. The material was developed by a Professor of Civil Engineering at Carnegie Institute of Technology, James Romualdi. It clearly has many applications for moulding thin curved articles of concrete, and decorative sculptures using styrofoam moulds have already been made.

Expansive or self-stressing cement

We shall refer later in the chapter 'Mixing the Mortar' to a new type of cement that has been developed in the USA which expands as it cures. This has the beneficial effect of putting the reinforcing into a certain tension when the concrete has hardened. The growth rate of the cement is said to be about 2 per cent.

Prestressing

This is, of course, no longer an experimental technique. Pre-stressing is a well-tested and extremely promising method of reinforcing certain types of concrete vessels. So far it has been used mainly for large structures and bridges, barge and pontoon construction, and its future in this field seems limitless. Whereas the ferro-cement technique of construction is ideally suited to thin curved hulls, pre-stressing is superior for flat bottom straightsided hulls such as barges. For example, although using the ferro-cement technique, Windboats Ltd, Norfolk, have used prestressing in the construction of their flat bottomed houseboat hulls, and Ferro Cement Ltd, New Zealand are also well experienced in pre-stressing boat hulls, and hold several important patents.

Another firm who have been quick to see the merits of pre-stressing for concrete barge construction is the Luzon Stevedoring Co. of the Philippines. They use their pre-stressed barges for inter-island chores and they have proved resilient enough to withstand a collision with a freighter and several all-steel barges.

These particular barges (engineered by Alfred A. Yee Associates) are 200 feet long, 55⅔ feet wide, and 12 to 14 feet deep.

Development in this field is well advanced in the USA and altogether hundreds of pre-stressed concrete barges and pontoons have been built around the world.

Pre-stressing certainly permits the use of thinner hulls, decks, etc., than would be possible with ordinary reinforced concrete and is a very significant development. It would not be out of place to quote here some visionary words from the inventor of pre-stressing, Eugene Freyssinet, made on the occasion of his jubilee as an engineer:

'Pre-stressing will enable us to build ships of such dimensions that the biggest waves will be only a choppy sea to them; immense floating breakwaters, thanks to which we shall seek not easy foundations but great depths for our harbours. These break-waters will be fixed to cliffs, making regions where the construction of ports was reputed impossible, much more favourable; floating islands will thus be made carrying prodigious machinery for extracting precious minerals from the depths of the sea. It is pre-stressing which will enable us to achieve the impossible task of capturing the energy of the wind and the sun and will build the launching ramps for our space ships.'

The lightness and strength of pre-stressed concrete have even led two Frenchmen, E. Freyssinet and Louis Brequet to experiment with its use for the wings of guided missiles and fighter craft! A detailed account, and the only published reference to this work known to the authors, appeared in the *Indian Concrete Journal* of February 15, 1954.

Pre-stressing is still a relatively new discovery which promises a great future as a reinforcing technique for large concrete vessels. Submarines and underwater cargo carriers might well be built some day in this medium. Many engineers believe that a good case can be made for the use of concrete for underwater vessels. Concrete, after all, withstands compression extremely well and is here at no weight disadvantage against steel. It would probably be cheaper to construct large cigar-like vessels in pre-stressed concrete than in steel plate.

We feel that the last chapter has by no means been written on the construction of large concrete ships.

CHAPTER 4

Ferro-cement boats versus wood, steel and fibreglass

Although it is possible to build very small boats of ferro-cement, it is not the best usually available material for such use. For pleasure and commercial boats, however, above say twenty-five feet, up to perhaps a hundred feet, this new form of construction offers many major advantages over existing building materials. In this brief chapter we will compare ferro-cement with the main alternative materials, under a variety of headings.

Construction cost

The cost of boatbuilding in ferro-cement is certainly considerably less than in any other material. In most parts of the world it will be found that such a concrete hull could be built for about two-thirds of the cost of wood, and often where wood is not cheap the margin of saving would be greater. As compared with steel or fibreglass construction, the savings would almost certainly be more again. No moulds are *needed*, as with fibreglass construction, although moulds can be used for ferro-cement where sufficient repetition makes them economic. Moulds, for example, are used in a factory in The People's Republic of China, where ferro-cement sampans are being mass produced.

Relative strengths

Ferro-cement skins, constructed as we indicate, have an astonishing resistance to high impact. They tend to be better here for boats than either fibreglass, or, for that matter, wooden planks of normal thicknesses used for comparable boats. In the chapter 'Case Histories' we give several practical examples of the material's qualities in this respect. Ferro-cement not only resists impact well, but it does not open up to admit water in the same way that would steel, wood or fibreglass skins. It has been found that the broken concrete remains in the affected area and impedes the flow of water.

Ease of repair

One of the most endearing aspects of ferro-cement hulls as we shall see later, is their easy repairability.

42

Relative weights

Ferro-cement boats usually can be built as light as wood or steel between the lengths of 35 to 40 feet. Hulls longer than this certainly can be built lighter than wood or steel, and comparable with fibreglass. Even if a small cement hull is a little heavier than a similar wooden hull, this does not necessarily mean a slower boat. It should be kept in mind that most wooden keel yachts have to be ballasted in any case. Ferro-cement is seldom heavier than steel would be, and usually lighter as size increases.

Maintenance

Provided reasonable care is taken in construction, ferro-cement needs the absolute minimum of maintenance; certainly far less than wooden or steel hulls. There is no problem of planks opening or closing under changing temperatures and moisture conditions and no continual battle with rust on steel plates. In this respect cement is nearly on a par with fibreglass, although of course paintwork has to be maintained; but primarily it should be noted, for appearance sake.

Ferro-cement is rot and borer resistant.

Relative building skills

Reasonable skill is needed to build any boat well. It does seem clear, however, leaving aside the highly skilled operation of hard plastering (this can be done by professionals in a day or so) that ferro-cement boatbuilding is within the capacity of the average practical man, with or without boatbuilding experience. A well-plastered ferro-cement boat is indistinguishable in appearance from a professionally built wooden hull. But a badly plastered boat can give the show away. It is important, therefore, for the amateur to engage well qualified hard plasterers if a high standard of finish is to be assured.

Fire-resistance

Ferro-cement, for all intents and purposes, is almost completely fire-resistant, and no normal steel hull could match this quality, since steel buckles badly under intense heat. One of the reasons that ferro-cement behaves well is that the reinforcing steel expands under heat at an almost identical rate to the mortar covering: the two are in close sympathy. Neither wood nor fibreglass, of course, has much resistance to fire.

Space advantages

Wood, steel and fibreglass hulls all require frames to impart stiffness to a boat. Not so with most ferro-cement hulls. Provided their shape is sufficiently rounded, to convert external forces into compression loads, ferro-cement hulls are usually

43

just as strong without even the pipe frames used to form the hulls. Even where they are plastered over, all that is visible from inside is a gentle swelling over the pipe frame. The great space gain for a small boat, which comes from eliminating projecting frames, has to be seen to be believed. A saving of between eight and ten per cent in internal volume can be expected from a ferro-cement as against a wooden hull.

Performance characteristics

Some characteristics of ferro-cement hulls have emerged, and these are interesting.

(*a*) *Vibration* seems to be less than for most wooden, fibreglass or steel hulls, when under power. The noise of water pounding or slapping the topsides is also much reduced.

(*b*) *Insulation.* Ferro-cement boats tend to be cool in summer, warm in winter. Heat transference is $\frac{1}{8}$th less than for steel.

(*c*) *Odour.* There is absolutely no odour once the cement has dried.

(*d*) *Dampness.* The writers have often been asked, 'Are cement hulls damp?' No dampness at all is apparent. There is no visible difference inside, between the under-water sections and those above water.

The concrete hulls made by Windboats Ltd under their trade name, 'Seacrete', are granted a 100 A.1 insurance classification by Lloyd's. Tests showed that their test panels had the following properties: similar test results can be claimed by Ferro-Cement Ltd, New Zealand for their material which is approved by the N.Z. Government Marine Department. The British White Fish Authority are prepared to accept applications for grants for vessels of this construction.

(*a*) *Density*

151 lb./cu. foot. (Mahogany 36 lb./cu. foot; reinforced plastic 100 lb./cu. foot).

(*b*) *Ultimate stress, tensile*

(i) Tensile bending stress on panels 48 inch × 12 inch × $\frac{7}{8}$ inch loaded at centre point:

Stress to crack	1,900 lb. sq. in.
At yielding	3,600 lb. sq. in.
At ultimate	5,340 lb. sq. in.

(ii) Tensile stress:

Stress to crack	1,300 lb. sq. in.
Stress to break	1,690 lb. sq. in.

(The ultimate tensile strength of high quality wood is approximately 6,000 lb. sq. in. along the grain, and negligible across the grain. Because mesh reinforcement is used, ferro-cement has similar tensile strength in all directions).

(c) Ultimate stress, compression

Compression tests on sample cubes 6 inch $\times$ 6 inch $\times$ 6 inch

Maturing time	7 days	14 days	28 days
Failing load (tons)	116	135·5	196·5
Ultimate stress (lb./sq. in.)	7,217·3	8,742·2	12,225

(The compressive strength of ferro-cement is far in excess of that of wood.)

(d) Young's modules

Modulus of elasticity—$1·30 \times 10^6$ lb./sq. in.

NOTE: The only tests so far carried out took place 3 years ago. They are confident that current production would show an improved figure.

(e) Bending fatigue tests

Four sample strips 21·65 inches long, 5 inches wide and 0·65 inch thick were tested. The distance of the loading point from one support point was 8·5 inches.

The results were as follows:

Sample	Nominal stress levels lb./sq. in.	Cycles	Remarks
A	+625 −544	$2 + 10^6$	Cracked
B	+700 −600	$2 + 10^6$	No fracture
C	±1,100	100,000	Cracked
D	±1,185	100,000	Cracked

The future

It does seem to us that for small boats above say 35 feet neither steel nor wood has the overall advantages of ferro-cement. Nor in many ways does fibreglass for larger pleasure boats, partly because of the high cost of precision moulds, and the greater need for internal stiffening frames.

It is interesting to note that at the 1966 National Boat Show in New York, although 60 per cent of all boats were built of fibreglass, of the fifty or more larger conventional inboard cruisers shown, fewer than ten were in fibreglass. On the other hand, more than four-fifths of all the runabouts were built in fibreglass, showing that fibreglass is still not too general for larger vessels.

The advantages of ferro-cement apply almost universally around the world. But it seems likely that it has a very special future in the undeveloped areas. Its low cost, great strength and durability, as well as the widespread availability of the raw materials, will surely appeal especially to people in areas like India, Asia, and the

Pacific basin, where good boatbuilding timber is so often scarce and prohibitively expensive.

The People's Republic of China has been quick to see the possibilities of ferro-cement and large-scale production of six varieties of concrete sampans has begun in a factory west of Shanghai, employing 600 workers. The conservative Chinese peasants, understandably reluctant at first to accept the new idea, soon realized its great advantages over timber, and the boat department is running at full capacity. This factory is certainly the largest mass production concrete boat yard in the world.

Ferro-cement boats can no longer be said to be experimental. Abundant proof of the material's great merits and durability is now available, and its future in boat-building seems assured beyond a shadow of doubt.

CHAPTER 5

Some case histories of ferro-cement boats

In this brief chapter we will examine several incidents which have occurred to ferro-cement boats, in order to show how the material behaves in practice. We quote only enough examples to make the point, since it would be tedious to repeat over and over the many similar happenings which we know have occurred.

Let us begin by relating the case histories of three modern British ferro-cement boats, built by a progressive company called Windboats Ltd, of Wroxham, Norfolk. This firm, under the direction of lawyer businessman Thomas Hagenbach, has pioneered ferro-cement boats in Britain and has built a great many motor cruisers in this medium. One is a 34-foot type called the Tradewind Class cruiser.

Tradewind 4 had the misfortune to be struck amidships by the stem of a 2-ton yacht doing about four to five knots (see Plate 9). The hull was deflected inward about $1\frac{5}{8}$ inches over an area measuring 2 feet 6 inches long by 2 feet wide. This caused a haircrack $\frac{1}{8}$ inch deep about a foot from the impact. All that was needed to straighten out the damage was to push back the depressed area, using a hydraulic jack braced against the engine bearers. This straightened out the dent and, when two small haircracks were filled and the area repainted, the job was completed. *The time taken for the whole repair: less than thirty minutes.*

Windboats Ltd consider that if the boat had been made of wood at least four planks would have to have been replaced.

In 1964, another of this company's hire boats—a twenty-four foot cruiser—exploded and caught fire on the Norfolk Broads (see Plate 10). The boat's cabin top was thrown fifty feet into the air and the mast landed in a garden 200 yards away! Fire ravaged the boat and the whole interior was completely gutted.

The explosion caused cracks at the transom corners, on one side, the maximum gap being $1\frac{1}{2}$ inches tapering to nothing over 2 feet, and on the other it was $\frac{3}{4}$ inch at its maximum point; both easily repairable. There is no question that a wooden hull would have been burnt to the water line and neither fibreglass nor steel could have withstood such heat without severe damage.

Windboats Ltd quote yet another story of a collision with one of their boats on the crowded waters of the Broads where the boats are frequently hired out. In this case a 34-foot ferro-cement cruiser *Classic* was struck amidships by the bow of a $3\frac{1}{2}$-ton yacht *Flight* 3, travelling at ten to eleven miles an hour (see Plate 11). *Classic's* hull was deflected inward over an area 7 feet long by 3 feet wide. The hull was jacked out and the damaged surface cut away, new reinforcement fixed and the area re-plastered and painted. All this took only twenty-one man-hours to complete.

A consulting engineer and marine surveyor, Mr H. B. Roberts, who was called in on behalf of an insurance company, has gone on record in a letter to Windboats Ltd as saying: 'In my opinion had *Classic* been constructed of timber in the normal manner, *Flight* 3 would have penetrated to such an extent that she would no doubt have sunk. Salvage and repairs under these circumstances would have been a lengthy and expensive business.'

Another case history, this time of a 35-foot New Zealand launch, built by Mr Rex Jackson of Wellsford, illustrates the material's resistance to high impact and stress. When being moved, the hull, which was resting in a frame raised a foot or so above several 44-gallon drums supporting her, fell over. The drums were squashed flat, but not even a haircrack in the hull was evident.

On another occasion this same boat was being launched under primitive conditions over a tidal mudflat. The cradle slipped and the boat was suspended for over a week, all its weight resting on only one point, until the tide was favourable. No evidence of strain could be found. Mr Jackson considers that a hull in wood, steel or fibreglass would not have stood up as well to such ill-treatment.

Quite the longest and most arduous voyage yet undertaken by a ferro-cement boat is that of the 53-foot *Awahnee* (Plates 13 and 21c). This vessel was built in New Zealand by an American, Dr Robert Griffith of Inverness, near San Francisco. *Awahnee* was built in Auckland after an earlier wood vessel of the same name owned by him was wrecked at Gambiers. The new *Awahnee* was built to the same design as the earlier yacht, but proved to be considerably lighter. Some technical advice was given by the co-author of this book, W. M. Sutherland, but construction was carried out by Dr Griffith, his family and other assistants.

Awahnee began her historical voyage from Auckland on June 25, 1965. She sailed first to Darwin, on the northern coast of Australia, and from there across the Indian Ocean to Capetown. Then she rounded the Cape of Good Hope, crossed the South Atlantic to South America, rounded Cape Horn east to west and sailed up to Hawaii. *Awhanee* battled through her share of rough weather on her 35,000 mile journey and weathered several 70-knot storms without damage.

One enthusiastic report of *Awhanee's* behaviour reached New Zealand after four months' voyaging, from one of her crew, K. W. Hingston. 'She is absolutely dry', he said, and added as if in wonderment, 'There is never any bilge water'. Dr Griffith himself is reported to be happy with his sturdy yacht's performance and is, we understand, writing a book on his experiences. His voyage was a noteworthy yachting achievement.

Another successful New Zealand-built ferro-cement ocean cruiser is the 55-foot *Falcon* (Plates 5a, 6 and 15b). In 1966, during the 1,300-mile Auckland to Suva ocean yacht race, a terrible storm blew up, and the entrants battled it for several days. So bad was the weather that one large yacht sank after springing several planks (fortunately without loss of life), three were dismasted and many returned

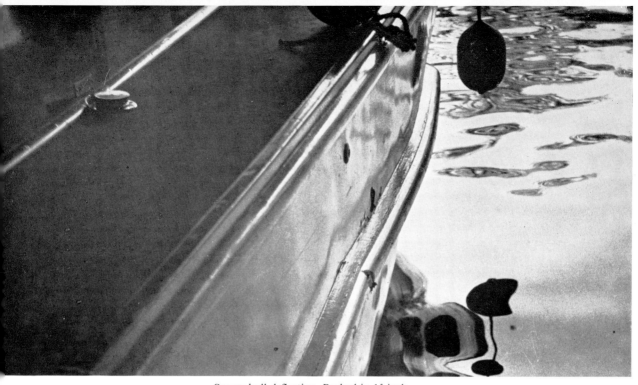

Severe hull deflection. Pushed in 1⅝ inch

and *b* On May 17, 1964, the motor cruiser *Tradewind 4*, a 34-foot 'Seacrete' hulled cruiser, was struck amidships by the stem of the auxiliary yacht *Lucky Breeze 2*. This 2-ton yacht hit the cruiser at an estimated speed of 4 to 5 knots. The area of the hull deflected from true was 2 feet 6 inches long and 2 feet wide. At the point of impact the hull was pushed in 1⅝ inches. Notice above the deflection of the hull, and below, the very slight surface damage—a haircrack ⅛ inch deep below the rubbing strake and slight flaking of the surface not deeper than ⅛ inch about 12 inches from the point of impact. To repair the damage a hydraulic jack braced against the engine bearers was used. It pushed out the hull to the correct shape. There were two small hair cracks, only ⅛ inch deep, these were filled and the whole repair took less than 30 minutes! With a timber hull, it is likely that four planks would have had to be replaced.

Photos: Windboats Ltd and T. M. Hagenbach

Notice the very slight surface damage

Photo: Eastern Daily Press

10*a*, *b*, *c* On August 24, 1964, the motor cruiser *Mars*, a 24-foot 'Seacrete' hulled cruiser exploded and caught fire on the Norfo
Broads. The explosion blew the boat's cabin top 50 feet into the air. The mast landed in a garden 200 yards away.
According to eye witnesses, after the explosion 'the boat was a blazing inferno'. The whole of the interior was gutted b
fire. The explosion caused cracks at the transom corners. On the port side the crack was $1\frac{1}{2}$ inch wide at the top, taper
over 24 inches to nothing and on the starboard side was $\frac{3}{4}$ inch wide, tapering over 24 inches to nothing. Other than th
above, neither the explosion nor the fire caused any damage to the hull. It is considered that a timber hull would have
been burnt to water line or a hull in steel or glass fibre would have been so damaged that it would have sunk.

Top: Firemen survey the intact hull.   Bottom left: Interior gutted by fire.

Bottom right: Illustration shows limit of damage.

11*a, b, c* On September 17, 1964, M.C. *Classic* a 34-foot 'Seacrete' hulled cruiser was struck amidships by the bows of the 30-foot sloop *Flight 3*. The stem of the $3\frac{1}{2}$-ton yacht struck the cruiser at an estimated speed of 10 to 11 m.p.h.

The area of the hull deflected from true was 7 feet long and 3 feet wide.

At the gunwale, the $2\frac{1}{2}$ inches $\times$ $3\frac{1}{4}$ inches rubbing strake was cracked and the mild steel angle iron $1\frac{1}{2}$ inches $\times$ $1\frac{1}{2}$ inches $\times$ $\frac{1}{8}$ inch was bent back 1 inch.

The centre rubbing strake $2\frac{1}{2}$ inches $\times$ $3\frac{1}{4}$ inches faced with $\frac{1}{2}$ inch $\times$ $\frac{3}{16}$ inch steel strip was completely sheared through and crushed and the hull pushed in $3\frac{1}{8}$ inches.

To repair the damage the hull was jacked out, the damaged surface cut away, new reinforcement fixed, the complete repair carried out, the surface sanded smooth and painted in a total of 21 man hours.

Top: Damaged section amidships.

Middle: Hull pushed in $3\frac{1}{8}$ inches.

Bottom: Repaired after 21 man hours work.

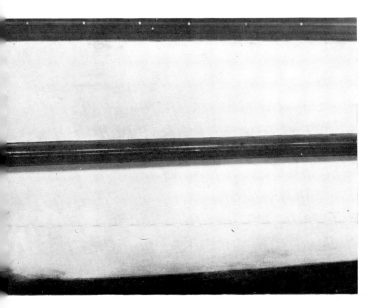

Photo: Windboats

12*a* Concrete motor cruiser in ice.

Photo: W

b A 38 foot fishing boat built by
  Ferro Cement Ltd.

Photo: N.Z. Herald

13 *Awhanee*, a 53-foot ferro-cement yacht built by Dr Robert Griffiths, shakes down on the Auckland Harbour before her epic voyage around the world which included a rounding of Cape Horn.

14a A 28-foot 'Seacrete' hulled twin diesel cruiser built under the supervision of Lloyds Register of Shipping and given their highest classification 100A1. Builders: Windboats Ltd., Wroxham.

b *De Zeemeeuw* (the Seagull) built in 1887 in Holland. Despite a chequered history, she is still in good condition, and now floats on the pelican pond at the Amsterdam Zoo.

15a Work begins on the lofting floor. Bending the pipe frames is the first structural operation.

b Frames being erected for the yacht *Falcon* at Ferro-Cement Ltd.

16a The keel of the 61-foot
     yacht *Veranima*, was
     cast in concrete before
     the frames were erected
     Frames were welded to
     steel lugs embedded in
     the concrete. Additiona
     reinforcement was also
     embedded in the keel.
     The fatty surface of the
     concrete could be etche
     with phosphoric acid,
     and treated with epoxy
     to facilitate a good bon
     with the ferro-cement
     shell.

Photo: Paul Farge

b Forward view of
   Veranima gives some
   idea of her size. Almos
   all the building was
   accomplished single
   handed. The hull was
   finished in three years.

Photo: Paul Farge

to New Zealand in a damaged state with sprung planks and cracked frames. All the entrants except *Falcon* suffered some structural damage. Not bad testimony, we feel, for ferro-cement.

We have already quoted in the chapter on ferro-cement the remarkable story of the world's first reinforced mortar rowing boats built by the inventor of reinforced concrete, Joseph Lambot, over a hundred years ago. Readers will recall how these two small boats were recovered from the mud at the bottom of the lake at Miraval, France, more than a century after being built, and for half of this under water. Both are still capable of floating, and one is in near original condition.

Yet another very early rowing boat, obviously built in a similar way to Lambot's boats (the thinness of the hull indicates that mesh was used), is still in existence eighty years after being built in Zeeland, Holland. (It was this province, incidentally, after which New Zealand was named by its discoverer Abel Tasman.)

The history of this boat is interesting. In 1887 the Belgian company, Picha Brothers (founded by Francois and Jean Baptista Picha), formed a subsidiary of their company called Picha-Stevens in Sas-van-Gent, Zeeland. This company was to be the first to make reinforced concrete products in Holland.

Via the canal from Ghent northwards and through Sas-van-Gent, ships can reach the sea-arm of the Western Scheldt, and so to the North Sea. Picha-Stevens (Stevens was an ex-mayor of Sas-van-Gent) were understandably marine-minded and as with Lambot forty years earlier, one of the first products they made with concrete was a boat; *De Zeemeeuw* (the Seagull) it was called (see Plate 14*b*).

The *Seagull* was placed in an industrial exhibition at Middelburg in 1887, among other concrete products. Such was the conservatism of the time that several reporters could see no future for concrete boats. One wonders what the reaction of these journalists would be today if they knew that this same rowing boat is still in use, floating on the pelican pond of the Amsterdam Zoo!

For the record, we would like to mention here a few other known facts regarding this historical boat. It appears that Mr A. A. Boon, Chief Engineer of Picha-Stevens, published an article in 1917, 'Der Bau von Schiffen aus Eisenbeton' (The Construction of Reinforced Concrete Boats), in the German magazine *Beton und Eisen* (also known as *Beton und Stahlbetonbau*). Boon expanded the article into a book in 1917 (edited by Wilheim Ernst & Sohn Berlin, and republished in 1918). He gives a short description of the boat but no technical information. He does, however, publish a photograph taken in 1910 showing the boat fitted with wooden decks and seats, now apparently rotted away!

In 1941 an Amsterdam contracting company presented The *Seagull* to the city zoo. It will be noted from the photograph how thin is the hull, and how excellent its state of preservation, after these long years.

A rather dramatic incident which speaks volumes on the strength of ferro-cement hulls, happened to a New Zealand boat at Whangarei. When a heavy engine was being lowered into the new boat, it slipped from its slings and fell into the hull, damaging the casing of the motor. No hull damage whatever resulted.

One of the earliest concrete boats built in the United States (a country, incidentally,

D

which so far has lagged surprisingly in the field of concrete pleasure boats) suffered an unfortunate accident. *Featherstone*, a Florida yawl, was forced into a sea wall by the wash from a passing vessel, damaging the hull slightly. A simple patching job soon put the vessel back in perfect condition.

Noel Holmes, an Auckland journalist, tells a nice tale about an enthusiastic ferro-cement builder in Whangarei. 'First', says Holmes, 'the owner established that he could knock a hole in timber 1½ inches thick with an eight-pound hammer; then

a

b

c

d

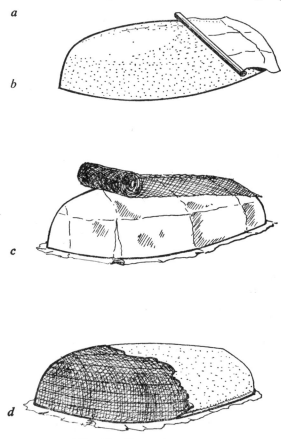

Fig. 10—Shoestring rowboat

(*a*) A rough and ready rowboat can be built from beach sand and cement as follows. Although not in the best tradition of ferro-cement, the form of construction is beautifully simple and inexpensive. It could conceivably have a military application.

(*b*) First form a mould of damp beach sand. Mix in a little fast-setting cement for the outer layer. Cover with polythene cut and taped where needed.

(*c*) Next cover with approximately four layers of ½″ chicken netting. Wire tie at overlaps and hold at gunwale with a band of No. 8 fencing wire. Additional bands of fencing wire over the hull add stiffness. Wire mesh to these.

(*d*) Finally plaster with beach sand and quick setting cement mixed 2 to 1 with a minimum of water. Plaster layer of approximately ½″, thickening to an inch at the gunwale, more at the keel. After two days, lift hull from mould, patch up inside and where possible sink boat to cure concrete for a few days.

50

he stood off and took a swipe at his boat. The hammer bounced off and nearly sconed (hit) his co-builder who was standing behind him.'

Galatea, is a sturdy 47-foot ferro-cement fishing vessel, built at Moeraki in the South Island of New Zealand. She fishes for crayfish on the fiordland coast there, and has proved very successful since launched in March 1965. Her work frequently takes her in close to a rocky coast, too close sometimes. One morning her skipper went to shave in the hand basin, and found that he was unable to work up a lather on the brush. To his dismay, he discovered that salt water instead of fresh water was issuing from the tap. He immediately beached the vessel, and discovered a cracked area, as big as a football, in the hull by the water tank. With a bag of cement he carries for such emergencies, he effected a repair on the spot, and carried on fishing. When eventually back in port, he slipped the boat and tidied up the job. *Galatea* was then moored, but by misfortune broke away in a gale, and blew on to the rocks again. The hull, slightly damaged, was permanently repaired with as little effort as formerly.

Recently, a 36-foot fishing boat operating from Whangamata in New Zealand broke adrift from her moorings one night and was found at daylight, her stern three feet clear of the water on a rock breakwater, twisting and rocking in a heavy swell. She was eventually towed off the rocks, and it was discovered that the vessel had sustained three holes of 8-inch diameter. These were repaired, after slipping, by one man in five hours.

'Instant boatbuilding' might make an appropriate byline for the story of how New Zealander Morley Sutherland built a small row-boat some years ago. Stuck for a boat to take on a holiday at the beach, he put two bags of rapid hardening cement and some half-inch chicken wire netting in his car boot. On arrival at the beach he made a male mould of damp sand and covered this with thin plastic, then laid several layers of mesh over it, and wired them together tightly all over. The mesh was then plastered over with a mix of two parts sand to one part cement, made from the cement he had brought and ordinary beach sand. The sand mould was begun at 4 p.m., and the boat plastered by 6.30 p.m. the same day. She was covered with sacks and left to cure overnight, and next day, late in the afternoon, she was immersed in the sea until morning, when she was used for the first time. Although understandably a bit crude, the row-boat added greatly to the fun of the holiday. Too heavy to take away, she was abandoned, but used by locals for quite some time, until blown onto a reef and abandoned.

So the case histories could go on. If one takes anything from them at all, it is that ferro-cement is very strong indeed. Certainly the owners of these boats all seem satisfied with their vessel's performance. From owners' accounts and from our own experience, these are the major advantages of ferro-cement over wood, steel or fibreglass, which at the risk of repeating ourselves we list.

1. Greater strength
2. Higher fire and explosion resistance (test panels have withstood 1,700°C for $1\frac{1}{2}$ hours with no effect on the material)

3. Immunity from rot, borer and rust
4. Lower maintenance than for wood or steel
5. Lower capital cost
6. Quicker to build in
7. Much less vibration and lower noise transference
8. Concrete vessels can become stronger as they age
9. More interior space, since projecting frames are eliminated
10. Easier to repair
11. Cooler in summer, warmer in winter (the thermal conductivity of ferro-cement is $\frac{1}{5}$th that of steel)
12. No leaks from joints opening up or shrinking as with wood or steel
13. Long life span. Even when made with crude early cements, concrete boats built a century ago have outlasted their wooden fittings and defied all prognostications that their reinforcement would rust through.

Although, lamentably, not every light concrete boat built by amateurs in New Zealand has been up to the standard your authors would recommend, it has become obvious from a study of their performance, that the material will withstand considerable abuse. There is, it would seem, a surprising margin of tolerance inherent in this form of construction. In this connection it would be fair to add that some superbly finished ferro-cement boats have been built by New Zealand amateurs who have taken the necessary pains. By and large, there is a wider margin for structural error in an integral concrete hull of this type than in a wooden vessel built of hundreds of separate pieces, each individually fastened.

CHAPTER 6

Setting up the reinforcing

The whole purpose of the reinforcing mesh and rods is to absorb the tensile forces created in the structural form. These forces are either due to:

(a) Shrinkage in the mortar

Cement mortar of normal characteristics shrinks when drying out and hardening. This shrinkage sets up a tensile strain which at a certain point the mortar is unable to accept. As a result a crack occurs, which releases the stress in the mortar. This phenomenon can readily be observed in, say, an ordinary unreinforced concrete path. Frequently one will notice cracks beginning to appear over the course of some months at intervals of about fifteen to twenty feet.

Now by adding sufficient small diameter reinforcing steel fibres such as one obtains from overlapping successive layers of fine wire mesh, these cracks can be replaced by many very small ones not always even visible to the human eye. The number and size of such micro-cracks will be proportional to the type, quantity and distribution of reinforcing used.

In smallish ferro-cement boats up to thirty feet, it may be possible to produce a hull without any visible shrinkage cracks, but as the size increases, it is probable that such very fine micro cracking may occur approximately every twenty feet. These cracks will not be serious, and what is known as heterogeneous healing of the concrete usually ensures their complete water-tightness. Nor will they normally depreciate the overall strength of the hull. It should be noted, however, that one can seldom avoid the appearance of crazing occuring over the outer layer of steel mesh which in reality is quite close to the surface. This pattern gradually appears as the mortar dries out, and has no practical significance. It is quickly forgotten once the boat is painted. When the mortar has reached its approximate maximum strength, the hull is in a stable condition and no further micro cracking should be expected.

(b) External loads due to use

All boats are subject to bending and twisting during their life, and it can readily be appreciated that although a normal rounded hull shape has considerable rigidity or stiffness, the mortar on its own has no strength to absorb the stresses so induced, and without reinforcing, cracks would therefore occur. Once again, the degree of cracking can be controlled by the amount and size of the steel used. As has been demonstrated later in the chapter on case histories, well constructed ferro-cement boats normally have much more strength than one would expect from a similarly sized wooden hull. When all the layers of mesh are wired on there is usually no unreinforced space greater than about $\frac{3}{8}$ inch in the whole hull.

By far the most common reinforcing technique used up to the present time is the system pioneered by Dr Nervi, an outline of which we have already given in the chapters on the background and the nature of ferro-cement. This system has proved very satisfactory in practice and is the one which is followed, with minor alterations, almost everywhere around the world. It is not necessarily the *only* method which would succeed, but in New Zealand, where hundreds of boats have been built following basically similar practice, we have proved that such a combination of mesh and rods works well. It is this method which we will look at in some detail in this chapter.

The mesh

The type of mesh one uses can vary somewhat, as we have seen, and may be largely a question of local availability. Perhaps the best type is a light drawn welded mesh of, say, about three-quarter-inch square pattern, although in New Zealand, where this type of mesh has not been available, we have found that ordinary half-inch diamond shape 19-gauge galvanized chicken wire laid in, say, eight layers has been satisfactory. Galvanizing has been found under test to be an advantage.

Although, as far as we know, expanded metal has not been used for boatbuilding yet, the work of Professor Wright, J. G. Byrne and L. D. G. Collen, suggests that it might be suitable, and rather fewer layers would be necessary. It is obvious, however, that where overlaps are made, the metal would need to be flattened somewhat to avoid undue bulking at these points. As mentioned in another chapter, Byrne and Wright recommend three-quarter-inch or one-inch mesh as a minimum size, to avoid a scissor-like splitting action apparent with smaller expanded metal. One would also have to ensure that the particular mesh was thoroughly pliable and capable of being shaped in complex curves. Test results of expanded metal are given elsewhere in the book.

Type of steel required

Steel can have very different characteristics. Mild steel is less good in stress than medium tensile steel and this less good in stress than high tensile steel. High tensile steel rod is preferable to the mild steels for this reason, but it has another greater advantage, and this is that it does not kink. When laid around the frames it remains perfectly fair; an ideal form on which to tie the mesh.

As far as the steel in the mesh is concerned, this is often produced from wire, which is drawn during manufacture, and such wire usually has good enough characteristics to resist the stress likely to occur in the spaces between the heavier rods.

Frames can be made of mild steel pipe, as these do not have much influence on the strength of a concrete shell hull, and are sometimes removed altogether after plastering.

Galvanized and ungalvanized steel in concrete

Some interesting experiments by Irael Cornet and Boris Bresler have been reported in *Materials Protection*, Vol. 5, April 1966, pp. 69–72, to evaluate the degree of corrosion of black and galvanized steel in concrete. They investigated reinforced concrete specimens, under a working load, exposed to corrosion in a 4 per cent NaCl solution under impressed d.c. anodic current, and under alternate immersion conditions. Quantitative measurements showed that under such corrosive conditions the galvanized steel retained a better bond with the concrete than the black steel.

Where to build

So much for a general background. Now let us look in detail at the practical aspects of starting construction.

The first practical job is to decide *where* to build. If a shed is available, all to the good, but many successful concrete boats have been built out in the open. Building a wooden hull outdoors creates many problems, fortunately largely absent from concrete construction. Nevertheless, open air building obviously restricts one's available working time somewhat. Rather better would be to build under a light polythene film-covered frame. Certainly a cover such as this is desirable later during the critical curing period, and obviously working under cover is far more pleasant at night and during bad weather. Excessive sun on one side of a hull can cause troublesome unequal expansion problems.

Forming the frames

The next job is, of course, to form the frames. One must first set out on a flat floor the full-scale shapes of each of the frames. A full set of boat lines always includes a table of offsets, and it is from these measurements that the shapes of the frames are determined. The pipe frames (¾-inch steam or water pipe is satisfactory for boats up to, say, fifty feet) are bent to these shapes. Naturally, one must make allowances for the skin thickness outside the frames. There are several simple methods of handling the bending operation, and suitable benders are available commercially. Each frame section should be welded at the joints and adequately braced to prevent distortion during construction. The accompanying photographs show how this is typically done.

As mentioned, the frame offers little structural advantage once the concrete has hardened, and where repetition of a hull is envisaged, one can remove the frames for further use. Normally, where only one hull of the type is to be built, the inner layers of mesh are wrapped outside the pipe, and the frame plastered integrally with the hull, so that all one sees from inside the boat is a gentle swelling of the mortar over the frame shapes.

The frames should be carefully marked with water lines and centre lines before removal from the floor, as this will greatly simplify setting up. For boats thirty-five

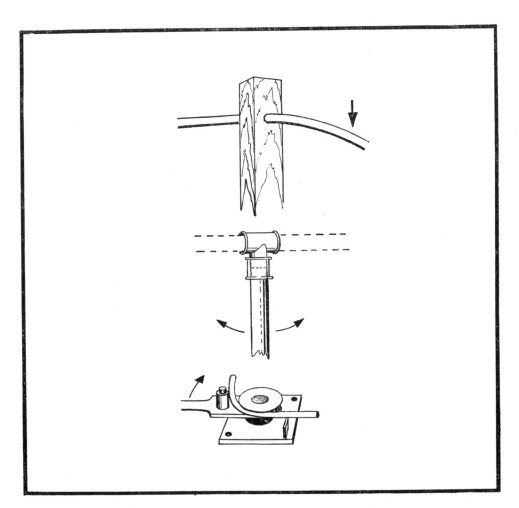

Fig. 11—Three useful methods of bending pipe frames.

(*a*) An effective and simple method is to pass pipe through a hole in a 4″ × 3″ wood post, and bend by hand.

(*b*) A 3-way pipe coupling (sufficiently large in internal diameter to slide easily over pipe) with lever attached, makes an effective portable bender. Two such benders used in conjuction, give one a good control.

(*c*) A commercial pipe bender with grooved former eliminates the possibility of flattening pipe.

feet and under, one sometimes allows for a slightly higher water line than for an equivalent wooden hull, or alternatively provides a little more buoyancy in the underwater hull.

Where the design calls for it, the pipe frames can be carried up above the deck line to provide stiffeners for a concrete bulwark.

The accompanying photographs should provide sufficient detail of the basic practice of reinforcement being followed successfully in New Zealand to enable an amateur to proceed with confidence.

Setting up can be done by hanging the frames from a central beam or standing them along the base line.

Placing the first layers of mesh

After squaring and lining up the frames so that the hull form will be fair, the first layers of mesh are wrapped around the pipe frames. In New Zealand half-inch galvanized 19-gauge chicken wire is used, and four layers are wrapped around at this stage. Each layer is lapped over the other by *at least* 3 inches, and the laps staggered with the previous ones. *These first four layers should be left very slack, as the stringer rods have not yet been fastened*, and the mesh will have to be pulled out to the hull shape here and there.

Fastening the stringer rods: Next the stringer rods should be bent around the frames and attached by wiring them tightly to the pipe frames so that they will not slip with the weight of the wet mortar. This is very important.

The stringer rods, as mentioned, are best made of high tensile steel. One quarter inch diameter rods will be found to be satisfactory for boats up to, say, sixty or seventy feet. Where the skin thickness is to about three-quarter inch, these should be spaced at about three-inch centres. Boats over, say, thirty feet should have a skin thickness of about three-quarter inch and rather thicker when they are nearing fifty feet and longer. Hulls smaller than thirty feet can be built with thinner skins of, say, $\frac{5}{8}$ inch thick. But one must be careful that the design of the hull will not permit excessive flexibility. The point here is that although the thinner skin is strong enough to withstand considerable impact, it does not give larger hulls sufficient stiffness unless stiffeners are designed into the hull. It should never be forgotten that concrete is basically a flexible material.

Usually the stringer rods are laid more or less horizontally around the hull in parallel lines, but sometimes they are laid parallel but diagonally around the hull, where this is easier or advantageous.

Where sharp bends are to be made in the high tensile steel rods, this can only be achieved by applying heat to the point of the bend. A portable gas torch is invaluable here. At these points the rods should be securely wired or welded to the pipe frames. *Welding the stringer rods to frames, however, is not otherwise recommended*, as this tends to reduce the strength of high tensile steel and cause distortion of the rods. Wiring on is much to be preferred except perhaps at tight corners.

Extra rods can be added on the inside if they are thought necessary. Such extra

57

stiffening is desirable over large flat sections, such as may be encountered under the cockpit area of a launch.

The method of cutting high tensile steel rods is somewhat different than for mild steel, since it is much harder. There are three basic ways in which H.T. rods can be cut. One is to use an ordinary hand bar cutter with specially hardened jaws. Another is to soften the steel with heat, and crop with an ordinary cutter. The third method is to hacksaw a cut about $\frac{1}{16}$ inch into the rod, place the rod cut uppermost over the edge of an anvil and snap the steel with several blows of a club hammer. So hard is the steel that a new hacksaw blade will be needed every time a new cut is made. This latter method is of course not used except in special circumstances.

Transverse reinforcing

Transverse rods are used in addition to the main stringer rods. They should be wrapped diagonally around the hull and wired tightly to the stringers. Transverse reinforcing rods can in some cases be of a lighter gauge. Their main purpose is to ensure a fairer form and to provide extra reinforcing.

Placing the outer layers of mesh

The outer layers of mesh can then be wrapped around, and joints should overlap at least 3 inches as before, and staggered one from another. All the layers of mesh must then be tightly wired to the stringer rods at close intervals so as to make a firm sandwich of approximately $\frac{1}{2}$ inch to $\frac{5}{8}$ inch thick.

Particular attention must be paid to the tying of the meshes. It goes without saying that all free ends should be kept inside the hull, and that no loose ends of mesh protrude outward. Take care when tightening the mesh that flat spots are not created between frames, particularly at concave sections.

Keel section

In yachts and other vessels with keel sections, the steel framework can extend around the keel section. The skins should be carefully tied together before any attempt is made to fill the keel section with ballast and mortar. To reduce weight in power boats, it is quite acceptable to incorporate some form of space filling material such as polystyrene or cork. Similarly, where increased weight in a keel section is required, a filling of steel stones or lead within the concrete could be made.

Fuel and water tanks can also be incorporated in the keel section, but where this is done these areas should be lined with some suitable material (see chapter on plastering), as fuel oils have a tendency to seep through concrete.

Engine beds

It is obviously desirable, where possible in the design, to incorporate engine beds as an integral part of the hull and keel section, but care must be exercised to ensure

58

that adequate stiffening of the hull is provided at this point, and preferably that the engine beds are supported directly off the keel section. Fixing bolts can be left protruding from the beds to accommodate any bearers that may be required and these should be made as integral as possible with the reinforcing before plastering.

The ferro-cement form of construction often enables one to widen the keel section out and accommodate the engine in a much lower position in the boat than would be possible with, say, a wooden hull with a heavy keel in the way. The advantages of this are that the centre of gravity is kept lower, more cabin headroom obtained, and a more horizontal drive to the propeller becomes possible. Thus widened flat keels could conceivably also have advantageous effects by inducing lift at speed, at least in light displacement hulls.

Fastening fittings

Fastening the usual fittings to a cement hull is really no more difficult than it is to either wood, steel or fibreglass. Usually one merely bores the bolt hole with a masonry drill, countersinks it where necessary, and fills up the surface with a rich mortar—or better still, an epoxy resin. In some cases, however, such as engine beds, it is desirable to build in fixing bolts or tabs before plastering.

When decks and bulkheads are formed from ferro-cement starters of the reinforcing rods must be lapped at least forty diameters to prevent pulling out. Reduced steel quantities can, however, often be used on bulkheads and other structural sections where strength is not so vital.

Skin openings

Any openings for skin fittings such as exhaust pipes, etc. should be formed before plastering if possible, but can be cut out by drilling or using a concrete saw.

Frame removal

If the frames are to be removed after plastering, they can be released from the steel framework by cutting the tying wires and cutting the frames at the keel where necessary. Care must be exercised in removing the frames if the hull is still at a 'green' stage. Additional inside plastering work will almost certainly be needed. Unless repeating a hull, leave the frames in and gain the additional stiffness they provide.

Moulding techniques

It is possible, of course, to use a male mould over which the mesh can be formed, and then to plaster either by hand or spray application. This technique would seem (largely because of cost) to be more suitable for smaller boats. It is worth noting that sprayed mortar is sometimes wetter than desirable, and the shrinkage is likely to be higher than with hand-plastered mortar. For this reason it has not been thought desirable in New Zealand.

In standard sections an external mould as well as an internal one can be utilized

59

and suitable mortar vibrated into the thin sections. This is the technique used at the Wusih plant in China where ferro-cement sampans are built.

Almost certainly, many variations of the methods described are possible, and man's ingenuity will undoubtedly devise them as time goes by. However, these techniques have proved workable, certainly for boats up to seventy feet.

CHAPTER 7

Mixing the mortar

It is not intended in this chapter to delve deeply into the chemistry of cement, or the theory of mix design. Such a study is hardly necessary for the practical man setting out to build a concrete boat. Nevertheless, it is essential for intending boat builders to have a clear understanding of some of the basic elements of concrete practice.

Concrete in general

It is not always easy to tell at a glance whether new concrete is good or bad. We are all familiar, however, with examples of shoddy work in buildings, lamp posts and so on, disintegrating under weather attack, and often exposing rusting reinforcing. There is now, in the light of modern knowledge, no excuse for this inefficient use of concrete. By following a few simple rules, and they are surprisingly few, these defects can be completely eliminated. Yet despite much misuse, there is no shortage of examples of good work over the seventy years since Portland cement has been in general use. Countless reinforced concrete bridges and other structures built throughout Europe, as far back as the early 1900s, are still as sound today as when built.

Concrete can, of course, be made within a wide range of strengths. Strong concrete generally requires more cement than standard concrete, and is thus dearer to produce. High strength mixes are not always called for, but where concrete is to last, it is poor economy to reduce cement, and the mixing and curing operations should be controlled carefully. For ferro-cement boatbuilding, rich concrete, or more correctly rich mortar (since only sand aggregate is used), is necessary.

Types of cement

Ordinary Portland cement is made from a mixture of clay and limestone (or chalk) ground up and burnt in a rotary kiln at 1,500 degrees centigrade. The clinker this produces is ground to a fine powder and then ground again with a small quantity (3 to 5 per cent) of gypsum. There are different types of Portland Cements, however, and each varies somewhat. The following are the main varieties in use:

Ordinary Portland Cement
Rapid hardening cement

Low heat Portland cement
Portland blast furnace cement

Another important type of cement, although not a Portland cement is, high alumina cement.

Each of these cements has different properties and several are suitable for ferro-cement boatbuilding, but ordinary Portland cement is by far the most widely used. It has a medium early strength development and does not generate as much heat as some of the other cements.

Rapid hardening Portland cement is ground more finely than ordinary Portland cement, and as a consequence gains strength more quickly in the early stages. It is useful in cold conditions, and where it is necessary to remove formwork quickly. Its ultimate strength is not very different from that of ordinary Portland cement, but it tends to set a little too quickly to be ideal for ferro-cement boats.

Low heat Portland cement is used where a large mass of concrete is to be poured, such as in hydro-electric dams. It hardens more slowly, and generates less heat when hardening, than either ordinary or rapid hardening cements. These qualities are not necessary for ferro-cement boatbuilding.

Portland blast furnace cement has rather similar properties to ordinary Portland cement. It differs in that blast furnace slag is ground with the cement clinker and this has the effect or improving resistance to chemical attack. This cement hardens a little less quickly, and generates a little less heat than ordinary cement.

High alumina cement is not a Portland cement at all, and is quite differently constituted. It is very dark—almost black. One of its major advantages is that it is very resistant to certain chemical attack and is recommended where such resistance is essential. Under no circumstances should it be mixed in with Portland cements. High alumina cement sets rather slowly but hardens very quickly.

Cement must be fresh, and stored in dry conditions. It should be smoothly powdery and not lumpy.

Development work on cements is, of course, constantly in progress, and two interesting new types of cements have appeared recently as proprietary products. One is a *shrinkage resisting cement* which has a growth rate roughly equivalent to the degree of shrinkage normally to be expected. The other is an *expansive or self-stressing cement*, which actually expands as it cures. The effect of this is to put the steel reinforcing into a certain tension, thus achieving an effect somewhat like pre-stressing. The growth rate, is somewhere around two per cent. Doubtless, more will be heard of these products in time.

Hydration and development of strength

Concrete is, of course, produced by mixing cement, water and mineral aggregates. In ferro-cement boatbuilding the only aggregate used is well-graded sand, and this type of concrete is called mortar. Here, as with ordinary concrete, the particles of aggregate are bound together by the cement and water paste which surrounds them and do not contribute to the chemical reaction within the paste. The reaction between the water and cement is a process known as hydration. Although rapid in the early stages, hydration normally goes on for some years, and during this period the concrete gradually becomes harder and stronger as long as it retains moisture. If for any reason, however, the concrete dries out completely, hydration stops, and so does the tendency towards increased strength. Resistance to chemical attack is also lessened. Fortunately, under normal conditions concrete retains some moisture for many years after being made. Painting concrete with suitable sealers helps in retaining moisture.

The following graph shows clearly how rapidly the strength of typical concrete increases during the initial month after setting.

The effects of temperature and humidity

Temperature and humidity play an important part in hardening concrete, expecially in the early stages. At one extreme, concrete and mortar laid at freezing point

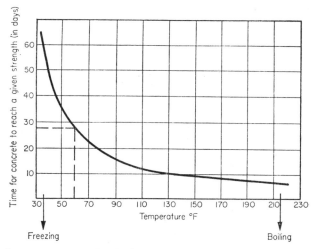

Fig. 12—Influence of temperature on hardening of concrete. Dotted lines show strength in usually specified conditions for twenty-eight days at 60°F

develops no strength at all. Many an otherwise good structure has failed because of sudden frosts. At freezing point, 32°F, the expansion of the water particles exerts enough force to break the bond between cement and aggregate and renders the concrete useless. At the other extreme, at temperatures near boiling point, very rapid hardening takes place.

The graph shown indicates how temperature influences the time taken for concrete to reach a given strength. If, for example, a concrete mix is known to have a crushing strength of 4,400 lb. per sq. in. at twenty-eight days when the temperature is 60°F, then one can follow how that same mix would take only seventeen days to reach a strength of 4,400 lb. per sq. in. if the temperature rose to 90° F, and so on.

As is generally known, the chemical reaction between the cement and water produces heat itself. If the volume of concrete is small, the heat rise is small, but when the volume is large heat build-up can become a serious problem. With small batches the heat escapes fairly freely, but when the mass is large the heat escape rate lags behind the heat build-up from the chemical reaction. This is a problem dam builders have to meet with such palliatives as cooling tubes to take away the heat from the middle of the mass. Fortunately it is not a serious problem to ferro-cement boatbuilders because of the thinness of the shells.

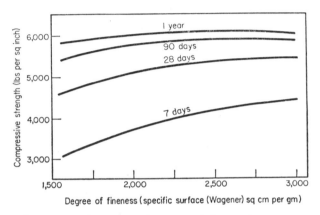

Fig. 13—**Finely ground cement gains strength faster than coarser cement.**

Incidentally, the warmth one sometimes notices in new bags of cement has no influence on a mix, except that it may perhaps increase slightly the rate of setting. Such heat is usually due to friction in the grinding process. The temperature of the water and aggregate in the mix tend to offset any effect which warm cement might otherwise have.

So far we have considered only the effects of temperature on strength development. Humidity also plays a very important part. Completely dry heat without moisture can do great damage to concrete.

Curing

It is important that the concrete be cured in moist conditions at any time, but it is vital in boatbuilding.

Curing Portland cements

(*a*) Ordinary Portland cement concrete must be kept moist for at least seven days and *high early strength cement* concrete for at least three days. Under very cold conditions these times could be doubled. Curing in this way tends to reduce

Photo: Barry Mackay

7a Inside a chine type launch *Arowhena*. Because of flat sections, extra stiffeners have been incorporated.

View showing how keel section can be widened to enable motor to be bedded as low as possible, and thus give more headroom and straighter drive to the propeller.

c At right, moulds in different stages of being covered with mesh. In centre mortar being moulded over male form. Sampans in foreground are being air dried, in rear, being steam cured under tarpaulins. Factory is at Wusih, west of Shanghai.

Photo: Courtesy of Concrete Products, Chicago

18a Cabins, too, can be moulded integrally with the deck and hull if desired. Wood is often preferred here as it is a little lighter and more attractive from inside.

b A Matangi 36-foot motor sailer ready to be plastered at Ferro-Cement Ltd. Note polythene tent rolled up above hull in readiness for steam curing operation.

19a A slump test being made. Mortar here is a little wetter than desirable.

b Rudder post, engine beds and grounds for bulkheads of a N.Z. fishing boat.

20*a* Plastering from inside a small boat being built upside down.

b N. Rodokal, manager of Ferro Cement Ltd, checks work on a Hereshoff designed yacht. In this case, pipe frames are being removed. Note engine bed.

1a A 24-foot Windboats Ltd hull showing floor and engine bearers. The technique followed by this firm is to weld lugs to the reinforcement to facilitate fixing bulkheads and lining. Practice in this respect usually differs somewhat in New Zealand. Note metal capping at gunwale.

Looking down into an H28 Hereshoff designed sloop. The skin is unusually thin and even the ribs have been removed, as the natural curves of the hull made them unnecessary. This vessel was built to a high standard of finish by Ferro Cement Ltd.

c A steel rubbing shoe was fastened to the keel of the ocean-going yacht *Awhanee*.

Photo: Seaspray Magazine

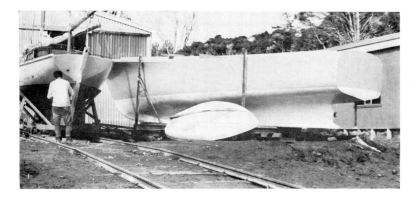

22a A cement motor sailer on the way to the yard to have her mast shipped. High standard of finish on hull makes her indistinguishable from a wooden boat.

b Co-author W. M. Sutherland's ferro-cement *Matangi* under sail on Auckland Harbour.

c An H28 Hereshoff designed ferro-cement yacht, alongside a 36-foot ferro-cement big game launch at the yard of Ferro-Cement Ltd, New Zealand.

23a A preliminary stage in the plastering of a New Zealand trawler. Note the bucket hoist and use of wood battens to give a clean finish to the plaster. Plastering of gunwale and decks will be done some days later.

Concrete deck, holds, and bulwark of a 38-ton mussel boat at Ferro-Cement Ltd, Auckland.

Photo: New Zealand Herald

c 'Seacrete', fishing trawler hull, $\frac{7}{8}$ inch thick, for Kenya, East Africa. 30 feet long, beam 9 feet. Floors and engine beds are moulded integrally with the hull. Lister HB3, MGR2 36 h.p. diesel engine installed. The vessel will be completed in Kenya.

24*a* Concrete ships being constructed at La Rochelle.

Photo: Vom Caementum zum Spannbeton

b A 3,700-ton tanker being built bottom up.

Photo: Vom Caementum zum Spannbeton

c A recent photo of one of several concrete ships built by E. Freyssinet between 1918–22 now in the Bassin du Commerce. It serves a small mechanical works. *Pouilage et Tournage* means pulley-making and lathe-turning works. The name of the company is Maison GAC Frères.

shrinkage, increase durability and strength, as well as permeability to water. The moisture level may be kept satisfactory either by covering the concrete with polythene, tarred paper or damp fabric, to prevent evaporation, or by continually spraying the surface with water. Dry winds, and the effects of sunshine must be watched closely. The work should not be allowed to dry out between periods of rewetting. If the polythene method is used this should be followed up before too long with additional water sprayed on.

(*b*) The temperature of the atmosphere must not be allowed to fall to, or below, freezing point, and it is very desirable that it be kept considerably higher, up to 180°F. The higher the temperature the better for Portland cements.

The ideal curing for concrete is to immerse the work completely in water at temperatures up to 200°F in accordance with a recognized time cycle. This, however, is not easy to do with a boat, and the best alternative would seem to be steam curing with low-pressure wet steam. Steam curing has the effect of increasing temperature

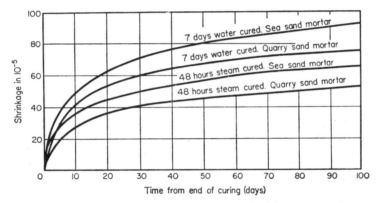

Fig. 14—Curves showing shrinkage of steam cured, compared with water cured, mortar specimens. (With acknowledgements to Ori Ishai and Nathan Bavli.)

as well as providing a moist atmosphere. It has a very slight tendency to reduce ultimate strength as against slowly cured concrete, but the difference is only marginal and not significant. But as shown in experiments by Mr Ori Ishai, and Nathan Bavli, steam curing reduces shrinkage by up to 50 per cent of dry air-cured mortar; a very important point this. Moreover, a steam-cured hull can be worked on or moved within twenty-four hours. By using this technique, a twenty-eight-day strength can be achieved in twelve hours. Steam curing is not difficult in practice, but a certain procedure must be followed. First it is necessary to cover the boat with a polythene tent and fill this with low pressure steam which can be produced by a steam-making machine such as is used in garages for car chassis cleaning.

No steam should be applied until the initial set of the mortar has taken place, as this can result in severe blistering. When the steam is applied, the temperature should be allowed to increase to 180°F over a period of two to three hours, and held

E

at this point for a minimum of four hours, after which the temperature should be allowed to decline slowly over a minimum period of about four hours. Extension of these times has a beneficial effect. Rapid increases or decreases in temperature can be deterimental.

High alumina cements cure differently. In their case, high temperature does not speed strength development and can even retard it. Because high alumina cement produces much heat during hydration it is less subject to damage at freezing temperatures than Portland cements. Moist cool conditions are important, and twenty-four hours are required for the initial curing of high alumina cement. Great care must be taken when using these cements.

Batching by volume

Although not as accurate as batching by weight, this method is satisfactory if care is used. But never measure the sand in terms of shovelfulls—this system, far too commonly used, can only produce erratic mixes. Volume batching must be done with the aid of a reasonably deep gauge box, built along the lines illustrated, so that the sand can be levelled off. It is not desirable to measure the cement in this way, however, and if possible a full bag of cement should be used and the other proportions based on this. If, for the sake of example, one takes as a suitable cement sand ratio 1 : 2, then a batch should consist of:

1 cwt. cement (one or two bags depending on weight)
        = 1¼ cu. ft.
2 × 1¼ = 2½ cu. ft. of sand (dry)

Thus a suitable gauge box size could be 1¼ cubic feet. Such a box could measure 12 inches × 12 inches and be 15 inches deep: not too heavy to be moved easily.

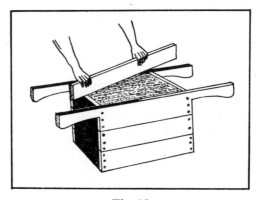

Fig. 15

Damp sand increases in bulk

Another factor to be taken into account when mixing mortar by the volume batching method is the tendency of damp sand to increase in bulk. Dry sand will occupy less space (sometimes even as much as 25 per cent less) than wet sand (but not saturated). Obviously, if a consistent mix is to be made, allowance must be made for this fact. One practical way is to shovel all the sand from the damp part of the pile first (usually this is found at the bottom) and decrease the proportion of cement and other ingredients to compensate. With drier parts of the pile (usually found at the top, especially in sunny weather) the bulking will have been less, and the proportions of cement and additives should be adjusted accordingly. *Better still, one can thoroughly wet the whole pile so that its water content is uniform.*

If one wants to make an accurate assessment of the degree of bulking that may have occurred, a simple test is available. The test is based on the fact that *saturated* sand occupies the same volume as dry sand, whereas damp sand with a water content

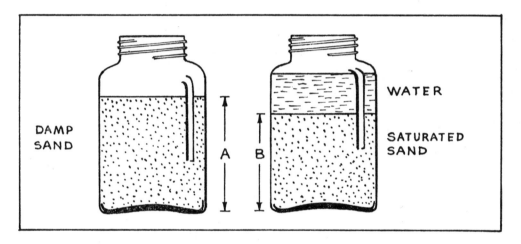

Fig. 16

between these extremes, increases in volume. To test the amount of bulking, take a glass jar and fill it about three quarters full with damp sand and level the sand off. Measure the depth of sand. Empty the sand into another container, and half fill the original container with water. Next, slowly tip the sand from the second container back into the first, so that it is saturated. Prod the sand to eliminate air bubbles as it is poured into the water. Measure the depth of sand again and it will be found to be less than when it was merely damp. The amount of bulking which has occurred in the damp sand can be calculated by a formula. Supposing the measurement of A to be 5 inches and the measurement of B, 4 inches.

$$\frac{(5-4) \times 100}{4} = \frac{1 \times 100}{4} = 25\%$$

It need hardly be stated that this figure is accurate only if the sample of damp sand tested is representative of the sand pile as a whole. But even if, for various reasons, the test is not completely accurate, it is a useful guide for the mixer operator.

Batching by weight

This is the most accurate method of obtaining the correct proportions of aggregate and cement, and is becoming increasingly widespread nowadays. Formerly the method was used only on big construction jobs and by highly mechanized ready-mixed concrete firms, but today it is standard practice where high grade concrete is desired. Batching by weight is recommended where possible.

A standard platform scale would be suitable for small boatbuilding work. Its accuracy can be tested by checking the reading against the known weight of a bag of cement. It is good sense to base the mix proportions on the weight of a standard cement bag, whether this be 56 lbs. or 1 cwt. Obviously, due allowance should be made for the estimated weight of water in the sand, but of course, unlike volume batching, no allowance need be made for bulking. If a scale is not available, a simple weighing device can be improvised by balancing a stout plank over a fulcrum at the centre and placing two full bags of cement at one end. An empty drum at the other end can be counter-balanced with an equivalent weight at the cement end, and in this way a two-to-one control can be obtained when sand is placed in the drum to bring the scale into balance again.

Water content

It is common to express the ratio of water and cement by weight, even though the water is usually measured for convenience by volume. Since the volume of water is in a constant relation to its weight, a conversion can easily be made. As everyone knows, one gallon of fresh water weighs ten pounds and thus a simple weight ratio between water and cement can be expressed.

The water-cement ratio is the weight of water divided by the weight of cement to be used in a mix. And the weight of water includes the weight of any water already in the aggregate. The following table shows this relationship:

Water-Cement Ratio	Volume of Water to each cwt. of Cement*	Weight of Water to each cwt. of Cement
	gals	lbs
0·40	$4\frac{1}{2}$	45
0·50	$5\frac{5}{8}$	56
0·60	$6\frac{3}{4}$	67
0·70	$7\frac{7}{8}$	79
0·08	9	90

* Includes water already in the aggregate. Example: $\frac{67 \text{ lb.}}{112 \text{ lb.}} = 0·60$ water–cement ratio.

Always use potable water for mixing. Sea water should be avoided. It does not materially affect compressive strength, but the salts tend to encourage rust in the reinforcing.

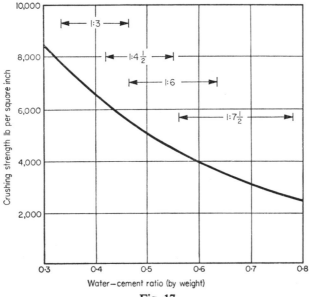

Fig. 17

The quantity of water in a mix has a considerable bearing on the strength of the concrete produced. Simply stated, the rule is this: a low water-cement ratio increases strength, a high water-cement ratio decreases strength. But obviously there must come a point where the water content can be too low. The minimum amount of water necessary to begin the process of hydration may still be too low to make the mix sufficiently workable to enable it to be properly compacted. Insufficiently compacted dry mixes may be weaker than well-compacted wet mixes at a certain point, as the following diagram shows.

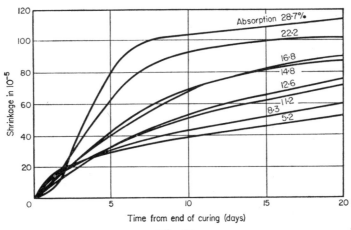

Fig. 18

69

Since sand almost always contains some moisture, an allowance must be made for this when calculating the water to be added during mixing. It sometimes happens that even as much as a third of the total water required is contained in the aggregate. Care should therefore be taken when adding water to the first mix.

The water content of aggregate can be measured where this is necessary, and there are various methods. One method is to weigh a sample of the aggregate while wet, dry it in an oven, and weigh it again on cooling. The weight loss after drying can be expressed as a percentage of the original weight. To be effective, the test needs to be done quickly, and fairly accurately.

Experienced operators know by the look of the mix turning in the machine, and by listening to its characteristic rhythm, when the right water proportion is reached. This is not to say that one should take no notice of the water content in the sand. Far from it; in practice one should see that the sand is either uniformly dry or completely saturated. Unless batches have a uniform water content one is liable to get differential shrinkage as the water dries out.

It is interesting to note, in passing, that commercial concrete mixers often have a meter attached to the driving motor. The load reading on the dial tends to be high when the mix is dry, and gradually reduces to a known reading when the correct water content has been added.

One must be careful always to add water very cautiously. A water-dipper of suitable size will prevent gross error. Keep in mind that it is not easy to go back when a batch, possibly already fully occupying the machine's hopper, becomes too sloppy. Nor is it easy to re-establish the correct relation again between the cement, water and aggregate if one tries to stiffen up the mix again. From the beginning of the mixing operation there is a continuous change. As the ingredients turn over, what at first appeared to be too dry a mix may suddenly change and come right, or even become too wet without the addition of more water. The lesson here is, watch the

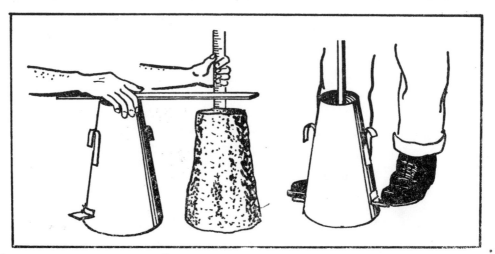

Fig. 19—Mortar being rodded, and after removal of cone, the degree of slump being measured.

mixing operation all the time. A little experience will show when the desired consistency has been reached. For boatbuilding, the water content of the mortar must be scrupulously kept to a minimum. Too much water will cause excessive shrinkage, although high water content is not the *only* cause of shrinkage.

One method of testing the workability of the mortar, which is widely used, is the slump test. To do this it is necessary to use a slump cone which can be made easily from sheet metal along the lines illustrated. .

One stands the cone, well cleaned inside, on a flat surface, and fills it with four layers of mortar one at a time. To compact it each layer is rodded with a steel rod about twenty or thirty times. When the last layer has filled the cone the top is trowelled flat. Any droppings around the cone are cleaned away and the cone withdrawn upward. The degree of wetness will be indicated by the distance the top slumps downward from the original height, which should have been marked. With a good dry mix, such as is necessary for ferro-cement boatbuilding, there should be very little slump, certainly not exceeding much more than 2½ inches. Excessive slumping will cause shrinkage, and could result in hair cracks during drying out (see Plate 19*a*).

The importance of good sand

Clean and well-graded sand is important if one is to make the high grade impervious mortar required for boatbuilding. Sharp silica sands are preferable, but not essential.

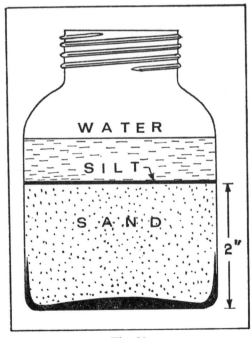

Fig. 20

Care should be taken, however, to ensure that the sand is not porous and likely to break down with time. It is interesting to note that some coral sands have been known to be attacked by tropical marine life. A little disconcerting, one would imagine! A rough test of the cleanliness of sand can be made by rubbing some between the hands. Stains on the hands indicate that silt is present. In this case a more thorough test is desirable, and this can be carried out as follows:

Take a one-pound preserving jar and pour in two inches of sand. Add salty water to one inch above the sand. A teaspoonful of salt will do. Next shake the jar and put it aside to settle for a couple of hours. When later inspected, any clay and silt will be found to have settled in a layer on top of the sand, and this should not be more than $\frac{3}{16}$ inches deep, and preferably no more than $\frac{1}{8}$ inch deep. If the level is higher than this the impurities may have the effect of slowing down setting time, and probably increasing permeability. If cleaner sand is not available, it can be washed by using a sloping ramp and fine wire screen. Such a device is not likely to be necessary in most industrial areas, but could be useful where only low grade sand is obtainable. Well-graded sand is very important. The grading can be tested, if there is any doubt, by using sieves of different sizes. Usually, however, one can gauge the grading sufficiently well for boatbuilding, by looking closely into the make-up of the sand to ensure that there is an adequate range of fine particles. But a sieve test is even better (see Plate 19b).

A test with sieves of different sizes should reveal a pattern such as shown in the following graph:

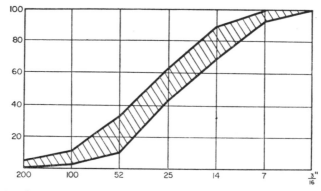

Fig. 21—Curves showing recommended range of sand passing through different sieve sizes. (With acknowledgements to Dr O. Ishai and N. Bavli, Israel.)

Concrete mixers

There are several different types of concrete mixers in general use. The most common machine used by jobbing handymen is the tilting drum mixer. Although satisfactory for general work, this type is not recommended for mixing mortar for boat construction. One objection is that a stiff mix, such as required for boats, tends to cling to the bottom of the drum and not become adequately mixed. Far better is the revolving paddle type, or the revolving pan and paddle mixer. In both of these the mix tends to be squeezed by the inclined paddles and workability is achieved with less water than would be needed otherwise. The latter consists of an open pan which revolves. Inside the pan, paddles attached to an eccentrically placed shaft revolve either in the same, or opposite direction to the pan. Both are illustrated diagrammatically.

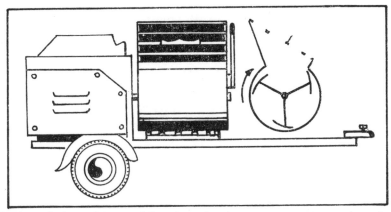

Fig. 22—A typical revolving paddle mixer showing a cross section as seen from end.

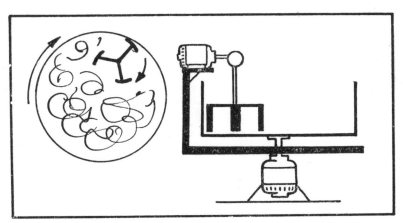

Fig. 23—Sketch showing basic principle of pan type paddle mixer.

Usually the mixer will be required for only a day at a time. and it is suggested that the average builder might find it more economical to hire, rather than buy, a suitable machine.

In practice it will be found that the mixer bowl and blades will keep cleaner if some of the measured water content is added first, followed by some sand. Then the bag of cement can be broken and its contents added, followed quickly by the remaining

73

sand, water and plasticizer. Pozzolana and any other additives should be dusted as evenly as possible throughout the mix while turning.

A matter of compromise

Mixing the ideal boatbuilding mortar is a little like mixing the perfect cocktail—everyone has his own theory. Within narrow limits one formula can often be argued against another. Certainly one has to make a series of compromises when designing a suitable mortar. The following factors may be considered.

A high proportion of cement makes a strong mortar, but one which shrinks more than mortar with a lower cement content. On the other hand, rich mortar produces a high-quality surface finish, and is far more impermeable than weaker mortars. Tests conducted by a researcher, Miss R. Friedland, show that dense plastic cement paste is the most important factor in protecting reinforcing steel from rusting. High impermeability is achieved where the surface area of the cement is higher than the surface area of the aggregate. This comes about when the mortar is rich.

Another factor is water content. A high water content reduces strength and increases shrinkage, but improves workability.

Plasticizers increase workability but tend to entrain air and can increase permeability somewhat. But because one needs less water in a mix when using a plasticizer, shrinkage can be reduced. Plasticizers, however, sometimes weaken strength. Which plasticizers are the best is yet another dilemma.

Yet a further factor to consider is the gradation of the sand. Well-graded sand makes a strong mortar, and one which is more impermeable and less liable to shrinkage than a mix using coarse sand.

Then, of course, one can argue the merits of different cements. Fast-setting Portland cements will have distinct advantages in cold weather where frosts are a problem. But they may be too fast in hot conditions, and cause the mortar to set before it can be properly faired and smoothed off.

So one can see from these often conflicting factors that there is room for some difference of opinion. Fortunately, the differences can be only marginal. One has to put first things first and make compromises. It is essential that the mortar be impermeable, which means a rich mix, using well-graded sand. To reduce shrinkage as far as possible, and increase strength, the water content must be cut back until the mix is only just workable. In our experience plasticizers can help with this problem of workability.

Additives

If one wishes to speed up the action of ordinary Portland cement, the addition of a suitable accelerator will help to achieve a higher early strength. The addition of a little true pozzolanic material in place of some of the cement can assist where the aggregate is high in lime content by combining with free lime to produce a better product. In New Zealand professional practice is now to discontinue using pozzolana as the aggregates used are of a high silica content.

Rather than lime, which has several disadvantages, we recommend a good proprietary plasticizer. One of the great advantages is that modern plasticizers require no lengthy preparation as does lime. Although most plasticizers have a tendency to reduce strength slightly, they do enable less water to be used and certainly improve workability considerably. They should, however, be used sparingly and in quantities only sufficient to make the mix workable.

Generally speaking, additives such as waterproofing agents should be looked at carefully. It is difficult to improve on high-grade Portland cement as an impervious barrier when mixed with well-graded sand for boat use. In New Zealand so-called waterproofing additives are not used.

Mix proportions

Some interesting shrinkage test results (shown below) have been published by J. G. Byrne and W. Wright, to whom we are indebted.

Shrinkage Tests

Cement-sand ratio	Neat	0·70	0·60	0·50	0·40	0·40	0·40	0·33	0·33
Water-cement ratio	0·35	0·40	0·40	0·40	0·45	0·50	0·55	0·50	0·55
Shrinkage	84	71	63	44	57	57	53	47	45

Obviously, it would appear that mortar made with a cement-sand ratio of approximately 0·50 (2 of sand to 1 of cement) and a water-cement ratio of 0·40, produces a satisfactory combination from the point of view of shrinkage. Mixes of approximately this type have been used by boatbuilders in many countries, and our experience in New Zealand would indicate that these proportions are basically satisfactory in practice. Dr Nervi has used proportions which are similar.

Such, briefly, are the basic principles of making boatbuilding mortar. Professional boatbuilding firms develop formulas of their own, and guard their secrets jealously. There is, of course, always room for improvement in everything, but lack of a little esoteric finesse should not deter the amateur. Rich mortar, made along the lines indicated, performs eminently satisfactorily in ferro-cement boats. Extra attention to mix design and reinforcement details can result in ferro-cement which has exceptional properties. But reasonable control of these factors will produce a hull more than tough enough for normal use.

CHAPTER 8

Plastering and finishing the boat

Plastering

We have already described how the mortar should be mixed. Depending on how many plasterers are engaged, so will the size and frequency of the batches be determined. It is preferable that the whole hull be plastered in one day. However, with large vessels this may be impossible and sections can be done independently; but if possible a sufficiently large team of hard plasterers should be engaged so that one has a comfortable time margin. Experience has shown that at least eight to ten men are required to finish a 30- to 35-foot boat satisfactorily in a day. Decks, cabins and bulkheads (if any) can be left for another time if necessary. If the decks can be done in one operation, all to the good.

High quality plastering, generally speaking, is beyond the 'do-it-yourselfer' and unless one has the necessary competence, it is better to stand by, or to handle the mixing operation.

It may well be that one is unable to assemble a team of hard plasterers with any experience in this kind of work, and it will be necessary, therefore, to instruct them in the fundamentals.

The most important canon they must learn is that the mortar must be used as dry as possible, consistent with working it through the mesh, and that water must not be added to the mixes they are given. The plasterers will have to work this fairly stiff mix through the closely layered mesh with trowels and this is hard work. It is *essential* that the mortar be thoroughly worked through the mesh and especially around the frames where air pockets can easily develop. One can work the mortar into awkward places with a gloved hand.

Plastering can begin from either side. There are, however, two advantages in starting outside. One is that the mortar does not have to be transported as far for a given result, the other is that droppings arising from trowelling the mortar through the mesh, do not fall into the boat and harden there. Constant checks should be made regularly to see that the mortar is being thoroughly worked through the mesh. This first stage in the plastering is by far the hardest job.

The inside of the hull is finally tidied up to a reasonable finish and if any bulkheads or tanks are to be plastered at a later stage they should be partly started to make them as integral with the hull as possible.

While some of the team are still finishing off one side, the others should begin work as soon as possible on the other. The outside is physically easier work, but more exacting. Here the mortar should still be kept as dry as possible, but it must be workable enough to enable it to be trowelled satisfactorily. Oblong wooden floats are used, and any other trowels and plastering devices that can be devised to fair the hull. Flexible wooden battens can assist in taking off high spots. Another tool useful in tight curves is the back of an ordinary tablespoon. Tradesmen, however, will know when and how to work the mortar, and so long as the importance of a high grade finish is stressed, all should be well. The final plastering is irrevocable and it is important to note this fact.

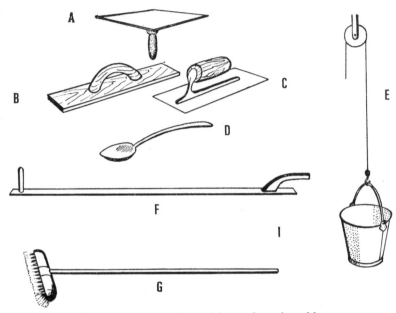

Fig. 24.—Commonly used boat plastering aids.

A: Hod. B: Wood float. C: Steel float. D: Table spoon, handy for tight complex curves. E: Bucket and hoist to carry mortar inside hull. F: Flexible batten approx. 3 feet 6 inches long, 2 inches wide, ⅛ inch thick (usually teak) known as a derby. Useful for eliminating bumps in sweeping curves. G: Soft broom, useful for taking off float marks.

Air pockets

It is probable that some air pockets will have formed during the plastering operation, particularly adjacent to frames and thick sections. These can frequently be located by gently tapping suspected areas with a hammer. A small hole should then be drilled to check. If a pocket is found, a creamy grout mix (cement and water only) should be pumped into the void. Wherever possible, obtain specialist advice and equipment, but if this is not available, careful use of a simple hand pump will suffice. Too high a pumping pressure on large voids will split the hull, and create further

77

problems. A series of further holes should be drilled around the area to allow the escape of air and to ensure that the grout penetrates the entire void.

Drying out

The techniques of 'curing' have been mentioned already in the chapter 'Mixing the Mortar'. We cannot over-emphasize the importance of controlling curing. One point, however, should be made here. As the water dries out of the concrete, the amateur may be dismayed to see a crazy crack pattern gradually appear on the hull surface. This may have no significance at all and can be ignored if the plastering has been carried out correctly.

Tanks and bulkheads

Water tanks, watertight bulkheads, engine beds, lockers and so on can be moulded with great success in plain ferro-cement. It is advisable however, when moulding in fuel tanks, to line them with a suitable lining material, as fuel oil and petrol have a tendency to seep through concrete. This is done after the concrete has dried out.

Fish holds are also probably best lined. Fish liquors contain ammonia, methylamine, hydrogen sulphide, oils and fatty acids which can attack the mortar, although experience shows that such attack is slow. Coatings are primarily for cleanliness. Low-grade concrete floors in fish processing factories, and ordinary concrete floors in fish holds seem to stand up to years of use.

Technical advice on suitable coatings available locally should be sought in all such cases. Brush applications of suitable epoxy paint, and a thin rendering of aluminous cement (ciment fondu) have been used by some builders. Heavy bituminous coatings could also be considered except for fuel tanks. Resin and fibreglass strands sprayed on simultaneously are better.

Jointing old and new work

If it is found necessary to join new work to old, the edges of the joint should first be brushed free of any powdery mortar. These can then be treated with an epoxy resin glue or with a thick neat cement grout. A little dampness on the edges will not matter. As far as possible, however, jointing should be avoided. If the old surface is smooth, this should be acid etched, say with phosphoric acid, and covered with epoxy resin glue.

Marine attack

Although the surface of poor quality unprotected concrete can be attacked by sea water over a long period, this is a very slow process indeed when very rich mortar is used and can be ignored. Moreover, normal protective coatings are quite sufficient to eliminate this problem completely.

78

Anti-fouling paints are just as useful for underwater sections on concrete boats as they are on wood or steel hulls.

There is some evidence that the micro-organisms which attach themselves to the bottoms of boats may provide some protection, and act as a barrier to ion migration, which is a factor in low-grade concrete corrosion. Not so seaweed growth, which can produce sulphur. Sulphur is known to attack low-density concrete but this is not a problem on a well produced high density surface.

Wood attached to *low grade* concrete can result in a fungus penetration under water, but here again this has not been apparent with high density mortar. An epoxy coat beneath any woodwork could allay any fears.

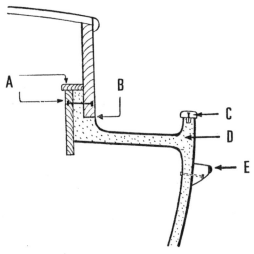

Fig. 25.—Detail showing common method of joining a wood cabin to a concrete deck. Recess in concrete is achieved by fastening a guide batten before plastering.

A: Wood caps. B: Cabin wall set into concrete turn up. Sealing compound is used behind joint. C: Wood cap. D: Ferro-cement hull and deck. E: Brass cap on wood rubbing stake.

Finishing

It has been found that grinding off the finished concrete to achieve a better finish is undesirable as there is a risk of exposing the reinforcing. One has to stand or fall by the form after hardening. The *texture* of the finish, however, can be made as smooth as desired.

Professional New Zealand practice has been to coat the outside of the hull with an epoxy resin coating. This has the dual effect of providing an additional water barrier, and of binding any surface movement of the fine particles of sand, thereby improving resistance to abrasion.

The last word has yet to be written on the painting of concrete boats, as it has with wooden hulls. One should seek the best advice locally in relation to the paints available. It has been found however that acrylic paints combine well with base coats of epoxy resins and bitumastic surfaces.

One final point. If an occasional rust spot does develop after launching, this will usually be found to be a wire which is too close to the surface. It has no serious significance, and can be eliminated next season by boring lightly into the spot with a countersinking drill and filling the hole with an epoxy resin filler. One need have no fear, provided reasonable care has been taken in construction, that such tiny rust spots will spread throughout the reinforcing. Good rich mortar is astonishingly impervious to water and makes a tough durable cladding to the steel.

If 0·05 inch of high quality mortar can be guaranteed over the steel mesh, painting can be eliminated, and coloured mortar may be sufficient for work boats. Because the control of plastering is not always adequate, painting is however recommended.

CHAPTER 9

Matangi, a 36-foot motor sailer

Shown here are the lines, plan and table of offsets of a 7-ton displacement motor sailer which has proved very popular in New Zealand waters. Several have been successfully built in ferro-cement, but apart from the suitability of the design for this form of construction, readers may find this section useful insofar as it illustrates how frame shapes can be determined from a table of offsets.

Matangi, designed by New Zealand's foremost yacht designer, R. L. Stewart of Auckland, has proved to be a happy blend of the qualities needed, both for good sailing and motoring. The design shown is for steel or wood, and in ferro-cement will displace more than seven tons. Mr Stewart suggests that, as a ferro-cement vessel of this size is a little heavier than steel or wood, the buoyancy should be increased by simply widening the centre line six inches amidships each side of centre, in a sympathetic curve. The moulds would then be based on two new lines. For further details readers are invited to write direct to Mr R. L. Stewart, 80 Paritai Drive, Auckland 5, New Zealand.

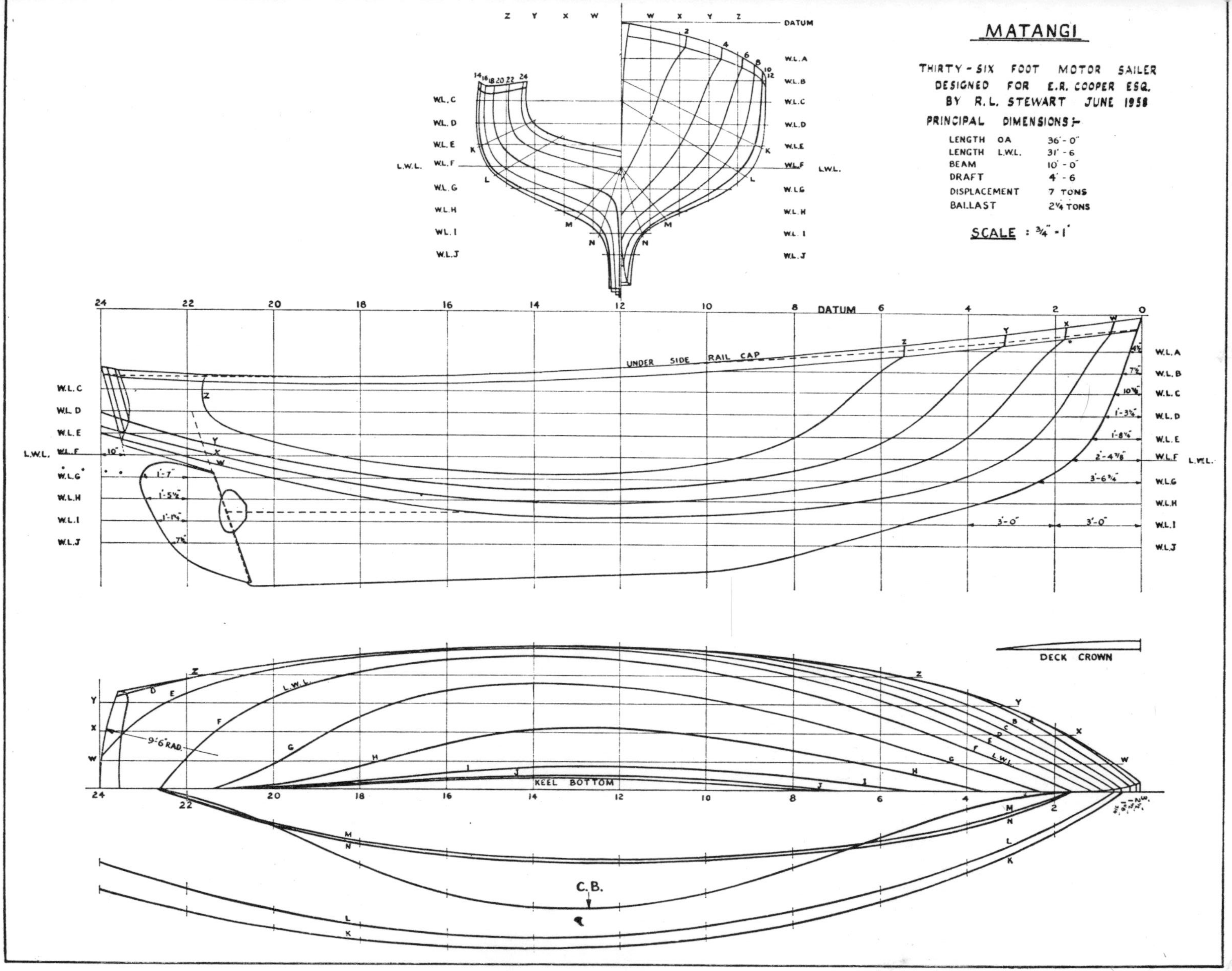

Fig. 26

WL.C
WL.D
WL.E
L.W.L.
WL.F
WL.G
WL.H
WL.I
WL.J

KEEL BOTTOM

C.B.

DECK CROWN

UNDER SIDE RAIL CAP

DATUM

MATANGI

THIRTY-SIX FOOT MOTOR SAILER

DESIGNED FOR E.R. COOPER ESQ.

BY R.L. STEWART JUNE 1958

PRINCIPAL DIMENSIONS:—

LENGTH	OA	36'-0"
LENGTH	L.W.L.	31'-6"
BEAM		10'-0"
DRAFT		4'-6
DISPLACEMENT		7 TONS
BALLAST		2¾ TONS

SCALE : ¾" = 1'

MATANGI MOTOR SAILER

TABLE OF OFFSETS *Lines to outside of Hull*

	STATION	0	2	4	6	8	10	12	14	16	18	20	22	24
From Datum	Underside Rail Cap	0.1.0	0.5.5	0.10.1	1.2.4	1.5.6	1.8.6	1.11.2	2.1.3	2.2.0	2.3.3	2.3.4-	2.2.0	2.1.0+
	Sheer	0.6.0	0.10.4	1.3.0	1.6.5	1.9.7	2.0.5	2.3.0	2.4.6	2.5.7	2.6.3	2.6.4-	2.5.0	2.4.0
	Buttock W		3.6.0	5.7.0	6.4.2	6.9.4	7.0.0	7.1.1	7.0.6	6.10.2	6.4.6	5.8.7-	5.0.4	4.3.6
	" X		1.1.4	4.3.4+	5.6.4+	6.1.4	6.5.2	6.6.7	6.6.4	6.4.2	5.11.6	5.5.4-	4.9.4	4.1.0+
	" Y			2.0.2	4.5.4+	5.5.1	5.10.4	6.1.1-	6.1.2	5.11.4	5.7.2	5.0.1	4.5.2	3.7.1
	" Z				1.11.1	4.3.0	5.1.6	5.6.7	5.7.0	5.5.4	5.1.1	4.6.2		
	Keel Bottom		5.5.4	6.8.0	7.6.3	8.4.7	8.11.3	9.0.4+	9.2.0	9.3.1	9.4.2	9.5.4	5.3.6	4.6.2
Half Breadths	Underside Rail Cap	0.3.0	2.2.7	3.5.4	4.2.2	4.7.3	4.12.0	4.11.6	4.11.6+	4.11.0+	4.9.1	4.5.1	3.10.7	3.3.1-
	Sheer		2.2.4	3.5.2	4.2.0+	4.7.3	4.10.4	4.11.6	4.11.6+	4.11.0+	4.9.1	4.5.2	3.11.0	3.3.5
	W.L. A		1.10.7	3.5.0	3.11.7	4.6.6	4.10.4	4.11.0						
	" B		1.6.3	3.0.0	3.9.1	4.5.4-	4.10.0	4.11.6						
	" C		1.3.1	2.8.6	3.6.0	4.3.4	4.9.0+	4.11.6	5.0.0	4.11.1	4.9.1+	4.5.4	3.11.3	3.4.0
	" D		0.11.6	2.5.0	3.1.4	4.0.0	4.6.7	4.11.4	5.0.0	4.11.2	4.9.1	4.5.2	3.10.4	3.1.0
	" E		0.7.7	2.0.1	2.6.7	3.5.5	4.1.6	4.10.0	4.11.7	4.10.3	4.7.5	4.2.3	3.4.1	1.1.2
	" F (L.W.L.)		0.3.2	1.6.0-	1.9.1	2.6.4	3.2.2	4.6.0	4.7.5	4.6.4	4.1.4	3.2.3	1.1.4	
	" G			0.10.1+	0.9.6	1.5.0	1.10.4	3.7.3	3.8.4	3.5.2	2.7.0	0.11.3		
	" H			0.1.4	0.1.5	0.6.0	0.8.5	2.1.6	2.1.5	1.7.6-	0.9.6	0.2.0		
	" I					0.2.1+	0.4.3	0.9.7	0.9.3	0.7.0	0.4.0	0.1.0		
	" J							0.5.3	0.5.4	0.4.5+	0.3.1	0.1.0-		
	Keel Bottom		0.0.1	0.0.1	0.0.1	0.1.4	0.3.0	0.4.2	0.5.0	0.4.2	0.2.5	0.0.6		
Diagonals	Diagonal K		1.5.3	2.10.0	3.9.6	4.7.1	5.1.0+	5.4.2	5.5.3	5.4.4+	5.1.6	4.9.2+	4.2.1	3.5.2
	" L		1.2.4	2.5.5	3.5.4	4.2.2	4.8.1+	4.11.6	5.0.6	4.11.0	4.7.6	4.1.4	3.5.0	2.6.2
	" M		0.3.0	1.1.5	1.8.2	2.0.6	2.3.1	2.4.3	2.4.0	2.1.5+	1.9.0	1.1.4	0.3.5+	
	" N		0.3.6	1.3.2	1.9.7	2.2.0	2.4.2	2.5.2	2.4.7	2.2.6+	1.9.6	1.1.5	0.3.2	

Feet inches and eights

Fig. 27

CHAPTER 10

Ferro-cement fishing vessels

We asked an Auckland Naval Architect, Douglas Alexander, who has designed a number of ferro-cement fishing vessels, for his opinion on the suitability of the material for fishing boats, and he has made these following comments:

The fishing industry exploits a major source of protein in a world hungry for food. Yet this industry is everywhere beset by high capital costs of equipment and bedevilled by low effective utilization of this equipment. Ferro-cement construction offers many advantages over other materials traditional in boatbuilding, and will become extensively used in the effort to lower investment costs in the industry.

Simple and cheap form of construction

In the first place, ferro-cement construction is technologically simple and employs few skills and even fewer machines. This will commend itself to underdeveloped countries but should be no less important to more advanced communities. It utilizes a much higher content of indigenous materials, materials moreover that are low in cost. *This can be dramatically illustrated by the comparative materials inventory for a forty-eight-foot fishing vessel built in New Zealand where the approximate N.Z. value of hull materials is $1120.00. This can be compared with N.Z. $3000.00 for a steel vessel.* Sand, cement, wire netting and steel rods just about exhausts the inventory; add pipe frames, cement additives and tie wire and the picture is complete.

Trawlers: ideal forms for the material

Ferro-cement provides an elegant means of achieving a most complex form. Without presupposing the reasons, a full displacement moulded hull, typical of advanced trawler design, represents the apogee of form best adapted to ferro-cement construction.

The full curved surfaces with little or no flat runs, so typical of these hulls, fits into the demands of the membrane theory of stress, leaving only a few areas which the designer must endow with the necessary strength. To explore a little further into this, one must examine the significance of the membrane theory. This requires that the arching of a load-bearing member be such as to place the principal forces in the plane of the surface. In simple language, the forces are either compressive or tensile in the direction of the surface. Asymmetrical stresses from bending are largely absent. To achieve such a system requires strong anchors in order to resist the planar forces. *This becomes obvious if the case of a barrel stave is considered with its ends on the ground. It will easily flatten if the ends are not fixed, but will resist considerable loads once the ends are firmly anchored.* In these circumstances, the load-bearing capacity of the thin shell forms is very much enhanced. A well-moulded hull has heavily curved surfaces which generally translate smoothly into the anchors which are represented in the upper work, and by the bulwarks and top sides which constitute a beam braced to the deck element, and in the lower buttock areas by the keel section with its shelves and floors and bulkhead footings, which go to form a rigid and strong beam. The layman may regard this explanation as unnecessarily technical, but it does permit the engineer to systemize what may be empirically obvious from experience.

Insofar as cement is strong in compression, in combination with a steel matrix and thin section, it forms a shell of surprising flexibility and strength when used effectively. It can be shown theoretically that stresses many times larger than those tolerable under normal elastic theory can be sustained.

Ferro-cement's many advantages

To continue with the catalogue of advantages that now include:

its technological simplicity,
its use of low cost indigenous materials,
the ease of forming curved shapes,
its inherent strength when used on curved forms;

one must add some comment on maintenance and repair.

Ferro-cement vessels are simply painted. It is fortunate that in recent years the development of epoxy resin paints permit the application of a durable coating which is both protective and decorative. The maintenance of concrete surfaces thus treated is a much less arduous task than that imposed by steel hulls, with their urgent and insidious corrosion problem that demands constant maintenance.

It is equally fortunate that epoxy cements show a rare compatibility with cement mortars. So good is the adhesion of epoxy cement to even aged surfaces, that in other fields it is consistently specified as a co-joining material between aged concrete and the new placement of concrete. This property permits the easy repair and a patching of damaged areas of a ferro-cement boat.

Where more profound damage occurs, such as holing on reefs or by collision, there is a great simplicity in repair that is not enjoyed by either timber or steel vessels. The damage is often much less extensive than that imposed on other materials, and even piercing results in smaller 'gaping' with much of the cement mortar held up in the easily yielding matrix, often forming an effective barrier against a gross inflow of water. Reconstruction can be effected, as indicated in the chapter on

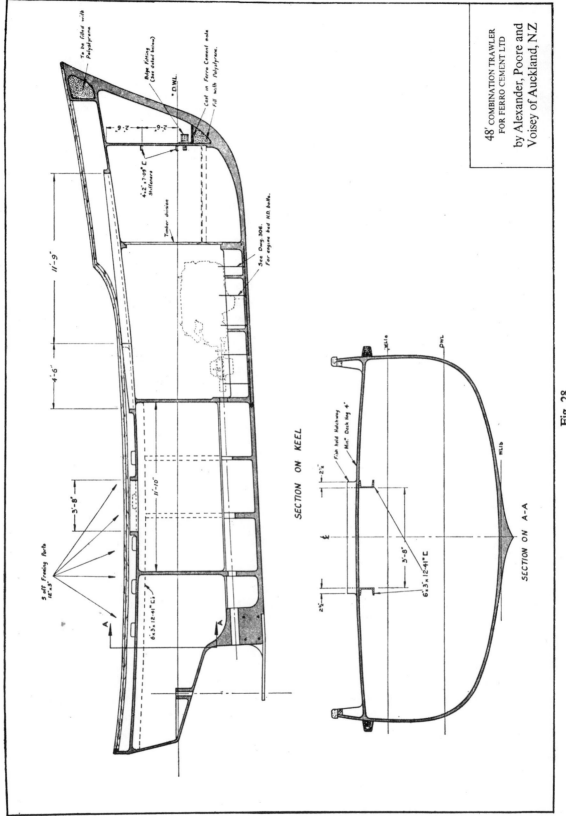

SECTION ON KEEL

SECTION ON A-A

48' COMBINATION TRAWLER
FOR FERRO CEMENT LTD
by Alexander, Poore and
Voisey of Auckland, N.Z

Fig. 28

'case histories' by straightening up the reinforcing and replastering, using epoxy resin as a joining material.

Ferro-cement is also astonishingly fire resistant, and can resist internal explosive forces very well.

Easy construction of insulated fish holds

One further great advantage of ferro-cement for fishing vessels, not yet fully exploited, is the ease with which both insulation and sound-proofing can be integrated into the hull during construction. This entails a sandwich construction of $1\frac{1}{2}$ inches of polyurethane foam boats, capped with a $\frac{1}{2}$ inch inner shell of ferro-cement. Both the inner and outer shells are cross-connected with shear steel to form a structural panel. This method of construction can be extended to include the bulkheads. As insulation is a costly item this method of integrating the insulation should greatly reduce the cost. Once coated with epoxy paints, the interior of the fishhold presents a smooth hygenic surface easily cleaned and maintained.

It seems certain that a great deal more will be heard of ferro-cement as a construction material for fishing boats, in the years ahead, and it is encouraging to hear that the Food and Agricultural Organization of the U.N. and the South Pacific Commission have begun development work in this material.

CHAPTER 11

Concrete ships before the Second World War

As already mentioned, the world's earliest reinforced concrete vessel was a rowing boat built in France in 1848 by the inventor of reinforced concrete, Joseph Lambot. Lambot quickly constructed others, but it was some time before large concrete vessels were built.

Although it is known that French Naval architects discussed with Lambot the possibilities of constructing large vessels, apparently nothing came of the talks.

Carlo Gabellini, a young Italian engineer, may well have been the first to build concrete ships. He began work in this field in 1890, and in 1896 patented several of his ideas. He is credited with having built numerous small concrete ships and pontoons. Among others he built a prahm (a flat bottom barge) of 90 tons for the Italian fleet which proved to be strong but heavy. One of his ships, the *Liguria* (150 tons) created a sensation by voyaging from Rome to Genoa.

Not long after this voyage, a Hanover firm built a concrete barge with a hull thickness of only $1\frac{1}{2}$ inches, and she was used for many years for transporting gravel. About this same time another German firm, Allgemeine Verbundbau Gesellschaft, which had been founded by an engineer, B. Nast of Frankfort, began constructing reinforced concrete barges. The company successfully built several of approximately 200 tons each.

A quite large German concrete ship, *Amoeneburg*, was built in 1918 for the famous cement firm, Dyckerhoff & Sons, and it is recorded she gave good service for many years on the Rhine and Main rivers.

The United States of America is known to have built a concrete vessel as early as 1892 called *Gretchen*, but no details are known to the writers. This ship preceded by a quarter century the First World War concrete ship building programme in the States.

Before the First World War, a Norwegian engineer, N. K. Fougner, patented several ideas (in 1912) and was involved in the construction of a ferro-concrete lighter in Manila. This experience enabled him to design a self-propelled concrete ship, and he submitted his plans to the Norwegian Department of Shipping in 1916. Permission to build the vessel was granted on March 31, 1917, and in the remarkably short time of four months, the 84-foot vessel, *Namsenfiord*, was launched with the aid of a floating crane. The little motor ship was successfully tested and began trading. So encouraging was her performance that the builders soon launched two other rather larger vessels, *Stier* and *Askalad*. All found buyers and proved entirely satisfactory in service.

Britain built her first concrete ship in 1910. Then during 1914–18 she became vitally interested in the construction of concrete seagoing barges owing to the grave shortage of steel plate which had developed. As a consequence of this, and the serious losses of shipping due to emeny action, a thoroughgoing building operation began under the instigation of Winston Churchill, then First Lord of the Admiralty. Shipyards at Aberdeen, Alnwick, Barrow, Barnstaple, Brighton, Greenock, Gloucester, Poole, Gourock, Monmouth, Preston, Newcastle, Shoreham, Stockton, Sunderland, Erith, Warrington, Queensferry, Irvine, Tilbury, Warrenpoint (Ireland) and Whitby began work on the programme of building seagoing barges up to 1,000 tons for transporting arms and ammunition to France.

A self-propelled seagoing concrete ship, the *Armistice*, was also constructed at this time. *Armistice* was built by the Yorkshire Hennebique Contracting Co. Ltd and launched in November 1918 at Barrow. This vessel was 2,500 tons and traded

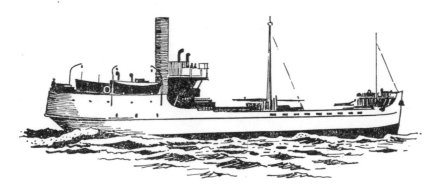

Fig. 29.—s.s. *Armistice*.

between Liverpool and Lagos without mishap of any kind, or missing a voyage, for over twenty-five years. The firm Hennebique also built a 1,000-ton dumb barge which in appearance was identical to a normal self-propelled ship.

The firm Hennebique of France was also busy during this period in the construction of concrete seagoing ships and barges, and built several vessels of approximately 300 tons to the designs of an engineer, M. Rudiger.

Soon after she entered the First World War in 1917, the United States embarked on a crash programme of shipbuilding. The production of steel plate could not keep up with the enormous demand for war materials of all kinds and America had also begun to suffer serious losses in her merchant fleet through enemy submarine action. The need for more and more ships was becoming critical.

It is not surprising, therefore, that the United States Shipping Board turned a receptive ear to the idea of building concrete ships. Mr N. K. Fougner who had

had such success with his small concrete ships in Norway, visited the States and addressed the Board. After hearing him they set up a concrete ship section to investigate prospects. Many other United States engineers and shipping authorities gave evidence before the Board and the US Senate Documents (Vol. 20; Doc. 239) of 1918 give an account of several contemporary reports.

The following table, quoted from the Senate Documents, gives an estimated weight comparison between concrete, wood and steel ships.

	Concrete	Wood	Steel
Hull	2,500	2,300	1,160
Fittings, outfit and equipment	191	191	180
Propelling machinery	206	206	200
Margin	75	80	60
	2,972	2,777	1,600
Reserve feed	80	80	80
Ordnance	23	23	23
Fuel	300	300	300
Stores	40	40	40
Cargo	2,760	2,180	3,057
Total dead weight	3,203	2,623	3,500
Full load displacement	6,175	5,400	5,100
Percentage dead weight to full load displacement	48	51	31

The concrete ship section of the USSB brought out a 'Special Report on the Advisability of Constructing Concrete Ships' in April 1918. The main conclusions of the report were that a concrete ship would last several years, its cost would be between $100 and $125 per ton dead weight, and that concrete shipbuilding would not interfere with the existing programmes of wood and steel ship construction. The Treasury, as a result of this report, made an appropriation for the immediate construction of concrete ships which was approved by President Woodrow Wilson in 1918.

Bureaucracy, however, as it frequently does today, proved too slow for private enterprise. On the west coast, a businessman, W. Leslie Comyn, having already unsuccessfully tried to interest the United States Shipping Board, was actually building a seagoing concrete ship when President Wilson granted government support for the Shipping Board programme. Comyn had set up a shipyard at Redwood City, California, and in September 1917 construction started. The ship was to be the first ocean going concrete vessel to be built in the States. *Faith*, as she was called, was 3,427 tons gross, 2,071 tons net, and driven with triple expansion engines of 1,700 I.H.P. which drove her at about ten knots.

She was launched on the March 14, 1918—six months after construction began, and only six weeks after the concrete had been poured. Her topsides and bottom were 4 to 4½ inches thick.

A remarkable article written by Mrs Jean Haviland (published by *The American Neptune*, Vol. 3, 1962) documents the history of *Faith* and the other concrete ships constructed at about this time. Mrs Haviland has very kindly given us permission to quote from this work and we are most grateful to her, for the information regarding American ships. Readers interested in a more detailed account of these steamers should refer to Mrs Haviland's very searching and readable history.

Once presidential approval had been obtained, the Shipping Board drew up a programme which called for the construction of twenty-two ships. As things developed, only twelve actually entered service, and all of them after the war had ended.

Fig. 30.—s.s. *Faith;* the most successful U.S. concrete steamer of first World War.

The first two to be built were regarded as experimental. One of these, the *Polias*, was designed by the Fougner company and was 2,564 tons gross. She averaged 10·5 knots on her trial run and on one seven mile stretch averaged 11·4 knots. The other, *Atlantus*, was slightly smaller. This vessel was 2,391 tons gross, but had an identical triple expansion engine to that of *Polias*.

Then followed the others. *Cape Fear* (1910), 2,795 tons gross; *Sapona* (1919), 2,795 tons gross, *Selma* (1919), 6,287 tons gross; *Latham* (1919), 6,287 tons gross; *Cuyamaca* (1920), 6,486 tons gross; *San Pasqual* (1920), 6,486 tons gross; *Palo Alto* (1920), 6,144 tons gross; *Peralta* (1920), 6,149 tons gross. Both *Palo Alto* and *Peralta* were built by the San Francisco company that had built *Faith*. Two more ships, the *Dinsmore* (1920) of 500 tons gross, and *Moffitt* (1920) 6,144 tons gross brought to an end the United States Government's concrete shipbuilding programme of World War I.

All these ships, six of them tankers, were constructed in normal ferro-concrete (as opposed to ferro-cement), usually reinforced with round bars from ⅜ inch to 1¾ inch diameter. Usually the concrete was composed of one part of cement (by volume) to two parts of total aggregate. A twenty-eight day compressive strength of 4,000 pounds per square inch was aimed at. Lightweight aggregate was used on several of the ships, consisting of a vesicular slag made by burning suitable clay in kilns to a temperature which caused bloating. Then the material was cooled, crushed and screened.

Understandably enough, there were many forebodings at the time that these stone ships would never prove seaworthy; just as there had been when the first Clyde-built iron steamer *Fairy Queen* was launched in 1831. We cannot resist repeating from Mrs Haviland's work, an amusing comment made by a negro who had been engaged

Fig. 31.—s.s. *Atlantus*.

to assist in moving *Sapona* on the short voyage from maker's yard to the outfitters. After taking one look at the ship he remarked caustically, 'I ain't gwine to sea on no grindstone'.

How did they perform, these early American concrete ships?

Faith proved to be the most successful. She sailed on her maiden voyage on May 22, 1918, and appears to have eventually gone out of service in March 1921, when a slump in shipping made her uneconomic to operate. She made many long ocean voyages and was eventually sunk as a breakwater in Cuba. Because she was finished at a time when she was most needed, *Faith* had the best record of service of all the American concrete ships, although not to be compared with the British ship *Armistice*.

Atlantus was put into the New England coal trade for about a year until laid up. She proved entirely seaworthy and was eventually sunk in 1926. Her remains are still to be seen.

Polias also entered the New England coal trade. On her fifth trip she went aground, and although a salvage attempt was made, she was never pulled off. There she remained for two or three years until she rolled off into deep water. As Mrs Haviland remarks, 'Old Cilley Ledge is in a very exposed position and it is quite certain that a steel ship under those conditions would not have lasted nearly so long.'

Cape Fear was commissioned on December 6, 1919, and placed in coastwise service. By the end of October 1920 she had sunk in a collision with a steamer carrying a load of granite.

Sapona was documented on January 8, 1920, and was also used in the coal trade for some time. Then she was laid up. Eventually she was bought by Carl G. Fisher, the developer of Miami, who traded off her machinery in return for some dredging work at Miami. *Sapona* eventually finished up as a liquor warehouse in the Bahamas until 1926 when she was blown on to a reef in a hurricane. There she still lies, frequented by fish, fishermen and skindivers.

Fig. 32.—s.s. *Cuyamaca.*

Selma and *Latham* were both documented in May, 1920. *Selma* suffered a whole chapter of accidents right from the start. She stranded, was temporarily repaired, then hit by another vessel, and was eventually abandoned. She is said to lie on the flats near Galveston.

Latham's history was also one of collisions and misfortune. After almost no actual service, she finished up as a floating oil storage tank at New Orleans.

Cuyamaca and *Pascal*, both of 7,500 tons, fared better, and did useful work carrying oil. The former eventually became a floating oil-storage vessel and the latter carried on trading rather longer. *Pascal* was laid up in 1924 and was still being used as a dismantled depot ship in 1932 at Havana.

Palo Alto was never actually used as a trading ship and her machinery was dismantled in 1926. By 1930 she was towed to Monterey Bay, and set up as a recreation and fishing pier at Santa Cruz Beach State Park. Although now beginning to break up somewhat, she has withstood the pounding of the sea astonishingly well over all these years.

Peralta was also stripped of her machinery in 1924. She was then used as a fish reduction plant until 1945. In 1948 she was moved to a mooring off Antioch, California, where Mrs Haviland mentions she was still moored in 1962.

It has been reported that the vessel has since been sold for use as a breakwater at West Vancouver, British Columbia. *Peralta* is certainly the oldest American concrete vessel to remain afloat.

Dinsmore was documented in 1921. She made only a couple of voyages and was then laid up. She was used for oil storage, and eventually ended her days as a breakwater in Texas.

In 1920–21 an American firm, the MacDonald Engineering Works of Port Arkansas, Texas, built two very unusual tankers, each of 298 feet (2,200 tons dead weight). These vessels were basically two long concrete pipes, each sixteen feet in diameter, placed side by side, and surrounded with a hull skin. The first one put into service, made only the slow speed of five knots and later when retarded by marine growth on the hull, her speed fell to three knots. Her performance was not encouraging and the other ship, as far as is known, was never commissioned.

Another concrete tanker was built after the war for the Quartermaster's Corps. The Associated Oil Company bought the vessel, *U.S.Q.M.C. Tanker No. 1* in 1923, and the name was changed to *McKittrick*. In 1932 this vessel was sold, dismantled, and used as a night club. A few other small concrete ships were also built for the Quartermaster's Corps but little is known of their fate.

In retrospect the trading performance of these ships was not brilliant, but almost all proved to be structurally sound, and several exceptionally strong. Their weight made them uneconomic as compared with steel ships, and the economic conditions of the 1920s so emphasized this fact that most were laid up. Structurally they were at least the equal of steel ships, although it is true some did suffer easily repairable weather damage in places where the reinforcing was not adequate. Nevertheless, the hulls of several of these ships serving as breakwaters in various ports still remain as silent testimony to the great durability and strength of the well engineered ferroconcrete of this period.

France, in the years after the First War built many ferro-concrete vessels, most of them designed by the great French engineer and pioneer of prestressed concrete, E. Freyssinet. By 1921 eleven hulls had been built to his design at Grand Quevilly, and another four at the Bordeaux yard of an associated company, Modern Maritime Constructions.

The characteristics of these vessels were as follows:

Length	180 feet
Total displacement	165 tons
Weight of concrete	500 tons
Weight of reinforcing	135 tons

Carrying capacity	1,350 tons
Density of mortar employed	3,792 lb. to 1 cubic yard
Coefficient of utilization	
(Percentage of deadweight	
to full load displacement)	37 per cent (i.e. within 6% of steel)

Freyssinet in a paper to the Congrès de l'Association Française pour l'Avancement des Sciences, at Rouen in 1921, reported his current thinking on these vessels, and on concrete ships in general. Very briefly summarized, these were his comments at the time:

(*a*) Perfectly solid hulls of reinforced concrete can be made, but those that had been built to that date had not all been equally good.

(*b*) Because with normal reinforced concrete there is a minimum possible thickness, it is more economic to build ships of, say, 10,000 tons than 2,000 tons.

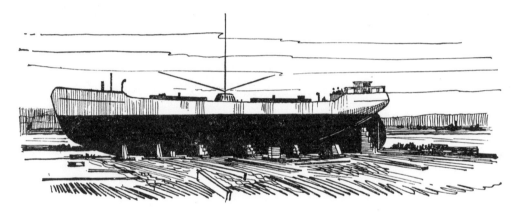

Fig. 33.—A French concrete vessel of 1,350 tons designed by E. Freyssinet.

(*c*) The reinforcing of a rationally built concrete hull should take the form of an ensemble of numerous steel wires of very small diameter being supported only by the principal strains in terms of tension, compression, and shearing. (It is interesting to note here that Freyssinet would seem to have been the earliest builder of ferro-concrete ships of any size to realize the great importance of numerous strands of small diameter reinforcing.) Other concrete ships built at this time were reinforced with more widely spaced larger diameter steel.

(*d*) Steel ships were lighter than concrete ships, but considerable gains had been made in reducing weight. The weight utilization on Freyssinet's own earlier ships of 57 per cent, had been improved to 67 per cent in later launchings. He considers that with improvements in steel metallurgy (high tensile steel had not arrived then) and in cement chemistry that concrete ships would have a promising future.

95

'From now,' he reported, 'hulls of reinforced concrete, which tend to be more economic, watertight and robust, and easier to repair than steel, commend themselves whenever the coefficient of utilization does not play a preponderant role. This is the case with port gear, cranes, lighters, dredges, barges, workmen's floats, floating docks, etc. As for ocean going vessels, one can only state again that concrete hulls appear less advantageous than those of steel because of their somewhat greater weight. All the same, it is not proved that the simplicity of keeping these hulls in good repair does not compensate for this shortcoming. But I am completely convinced that, in the near future, hulls will be built by the process of reinforced concrete, as light and lighter than ordinary hulls of steel. Their use will assert itself then in all branches of naval architecture.'

Freyssinet's remarks were certainly prophetic. We have seen that concrete hulls lighter than steel have come about with the ferro-cement technique as described. And although the ferro-cement technique has been used only on smallish vessels so far, there are signs that larger concrete ships, prestressed this time and far lighter than any built before in concrete, may not be far away.

Another war was to intervene, however, before ferro-cement and other promising new techniques were to make their appearance. In the next chapter we will see how the critical shortage of steel plate in the Second War again forced Britain and America into building ferro-concrete ships; better vessels, it is true, than those of the First World War, but still basically conventional in the method of their reinforcement.

CHAPTER 12

Concrete vessels of the Second World War

Britain built only two self-propelled concrete ships during the last war. The first and last concrete ship of the First World War, *Armistice*, had performed remarkably well for twenty-five years, and doubtless she was remembered when plans were put in hand to build stone ships once more. Both Second War vessels were built to the design of Sir Owen Williams, the man who engineered Wembley Exhibition, and it is recorded that he spent a year working out their plans.

'I do not suggest that all-concrete ships will ever replace steel ones,' said Sir Owen in a newspaper report at the time, 'but it is certain that there is a real place for them in wartime.'

'Compared with a steel ship of the same size, and with the same carrying capacity, my ship represents a saving of 40 per cent in metal requirements. Production costs are also far cheaper. I now have plans for a 10,000 tonner which we hope to put under construction shortly. As the tonnage increases so the economy on steel and labour rises.' This ship, however, was never to be built.

The first of Sir Owen's two ships to be launched was the *Lady Wolmer*, built by W. & C. French Ltd of Newport, Monmouthshire. She was registered in Bristol in 1942 and was managed by Walford Lines for the Ministry of Transport. She had a displacement of 4,000 tons and could carry 2,400 tons dead-weight. Both *Lady Wolmer* and her sister ship *Lady Kathleen* were 265 feet long, 42 feet in beam, and 18 feet deep.

Lady Wolmer was engaged in the coastal coal trade from South Wales to the west coast, and it is believed was later joined in this trade by her sister ship *Lady Kathleen*. *Lady Wolmer* it seems developed a few superficial cracks, it is thought from contact with a wharf, but her skipper has gone on record as saying that the vessel:

(1) was cooler in summer and warmer in winter than a steel ship;
(2) that she did not roll as much as a similar type of vessel built of steel;
(3) that he has found the vessel very seaworthy.

Lady Wolmer was removed from Lloyds' register of shipping 1952–55.

By far the most important British war application of ferro-concrete in marine use, however, was the construction of that great floating harbour at Arromanches, Mulberry 'B'.

The great concrete breakwater, and other specialized harbour equipment which were towed across, served the cause well. Despite many problems which arose, the concrete caissons and the ballasted block ships produced sheltered water suitable for navigation under almost all conditions of weather during the life of the harbour.

The breakwaters were composed of two different units: self-powered steel sand ballasted blockships and concrete caissons. The concrete caissons, with which we are concerned, were built in six different sizes. All but the smallest (which was 174 feet long) were the same length; namely 204 feet. They varied greatly, however, in depth from twenty-five to sixty feet. These caissons were towed over to pre-determined positions, and sunk at the end of a string of ballasted block ships some of which were self-propelled American concrete ships. Except at very high spring tides their deckwork was well above the surface.

The minutely detailed planning of the design and function of the harbour and caissons was one of the great engineering achievements of the war, and involved many specialized branches of engineering. Careful calculation of the complex forces of wave action was essential, and much basic research was carried out in water tanks, and in physical tests in actual storm conditions. When the minimum requirements of the harbour had been considered it was laid down that the components should be able to withstand gale conditions up to Force 6. It was felt that during the initial invasion period higher winds than this would probably not be met, and that it was a calculated risk to assume this. It was felt that dangerous wastage of material and time would result if an excessively high-strength figure were to be called for.

As things turned out, an untimely gale from the north-east did blow up, but after the invasion had well and truly begun. It lasted for three days, from June 19th until the 22nd, and the wind intensity often reached Force 7 on the Beaufort scale.

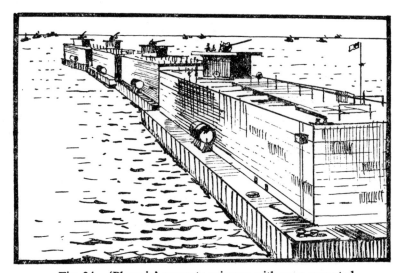

Fig. 34.—'Phoenix' concrete caissons with guns mounted.

The blockships, which were ballasted with dry sand, stood up with almost no damage, but the concrete caissons, because of the greatly different nature of their function, did not fare quite so well. Some units burst, although most stood up very satisfactorily. Those that did break up were all part of the western half of the break-water where the sea bed was most susceptible to scouring. During, or immediately after the bad weather, the sea bed scoured away, and some of the caissons, or bombardons as they were also called, settled at one end, and later broke their backs. Improved designs were developed but these do not appear to have been used, as a decision was made to abandon further work on the harbour, its need by then being no longer critical.

Some idea of the immense bulk of these caissons which, incidentally, were built under the code name 'Phoenix', may be gained from the following table of materials actually incorporated in the structures (exclusive of fittings). The figures were quoted by Mr Cyril Wood, M.I.C.E., in a paper published after the war.

Original Programme

Concrete	410,000 cubic yards formed from the following materials:
Sand	179,000 cubic yards
Aggregate	358,000 cubic yards
Cement	129,000 tons
Mild-steel-bar reinforcement	29,570 tons

Supplementary Caissons

Concrete	132,000 cubic yards, from:
Sand	57,500 cubic yards
Aggregate	115,000 cubic yards
Cement	41,400 cubic yards
Mild-steel-bar reinforcement	19,600 tons

These figures do not include the immense amount of concrete and other materials used in constructing slipways, basins, dams etc. as part of the Phoenix programme.

Originally it was intended to keep all the caissons floating until required but it was later decided to sink the leviathans partly as a means of concealing them from the enemy. They were later raised by pumping in air. Both the sinking and refloating operations also afforded valuable handling experience to the crews.

Caissons were by no means the only use of concrete in the construction of the port. Strong floating concrete pontoons to support flexible steel piers were also a very important part of the scheme. Concrete pontoons of many sizes and shapes were built, and these proved very successful. All were extremely strong and most were divided internally into a mass of concrete watertight bulkheads. Although often different in design, all the latter were known under the generic name of 'Beetles'.

Germany, it is known, built a number of concrete barges and pontoons during the war, including some at Drammen, Norway; built, incidentally, with incredible slowness, doubtless because of deliberate Norwegian heel-dragging.

As in the First World War, America led in the use of concrete for self-propelled ships in the Second. Again we are deeply indebted for information on developments there to Mrs Jean Haviland, whose research on the subject of American concrete ships forms a very basic historical reference.

There was, it seems, some opposition in America to the programme to build self-propelled concrete ships again, but shipping was so desperately needed, and steel plate in such demand, that a big scheme was started. It was apparently not thought wise to build large ships of wood, as had been done in the First World War.

In 1942 a contract was awarded to McCloskey and Co. of Philadelphia to build twenty-four self-propelled concrete ships. All were to be of 350 feet 3 inches long, 54 feet wide and 35 feet deep. These ships were to be used for the transport of sugar. Their displacement tonnage varied from 10,950 tons to 11,370 tons. They had ten transverse bulkheads, six cargo compartments, and three ballast compartments. Their 1,300 I.H.P. triple expansion engines were located aft, and calculated to drive the ships at ten knots.

The method of their construction was not greatly different from that followed two decades earlier, but they were much stronger, due partly to better cement, more steel and better mix design. The concrete used was one part cement to two and a half parts of lightweight aggregate, which was composed of Haydite, Modulite or Aerox (forms of burnt clay or shale) and 15 to 50 per cent of natural sand, depending on the composition of the clay.

The formwork was usually of $\frac{5}{8}$-inch to $\frac{3}{4}$-inch special oil-treated plywood. This was formed around the exterior of the hull first. Later, after the inside boxing had been built, the first mix was poured up to about 4 feet 6 inches elevation and gradually carried higher in successive mixes. All pourings were well vibrated and eventually the deck, too, was poured in concrete.

McCloskey and Co developed their yard near Tampa, Florida, and laid out space for thirteen berths in four basins. Vessels were launched three at a time by flooding the basins. As each ship was in a different state of completion, a careful study had to be made of the pivoting pressure which the incoming water exerted on the differently ballasted hulls. One hull developed long shear cracks (later repaired) before this difficulty was realized. With later launchings, ballasting and flooding were carried out simultaneously and the problem was overcome.

The first batch of three ships, *Vitruvius, David O Saylor*, and *Arthur Newell Talbot* were floated off together on July 15, 1943. Finally, on September 24, 1944, the eighth and last batch of three was launched, and with them the concrete steamer programme came to an end.

All the ships bore the names of great pioneers in the development of concrete or concrete products, some of whom we have already mentioned in the chapter on the development of cement. One ship, the *P.M. Anderson*, was named in honour of the colonel of that name who had had extensive experience in concrete shipbuilding in the First War, and who also contributed much to the same cause during the last war.

Very briefly, here is the history of these Second World War ships.

David O. Saylor was the first to be delivered to her operators. She was little used, due to a mishap to one of her oil tanks when too much pressure was applied in filling. Later she sailed across the Atlantic and was sunk at San Lorenzo beachhead, France, on July 16, 1944, to join the other specially designed concrete breakwaters there.

Vitruvius made two trips to and from Cuba with sugar. She, too, was used as a breakwater during the Normandy invasion.

Arthur Newell Talbot, documented on February 14, 1944, was sent to the west coast as an army training ship. She gave good service for a year and was then laid up in 1945. When the war ended she was sold as a breakwater at Kiptopeke, Virginia, where she still remains.

Richard Lewis Humphrey was documented on March 31, 1944. On her first voyage she sailed with a cargo of coffee to the west coast. She once sailed through a sixty-knot wind without any damage, although later she did develop some fine hair-cracks on her deck. She was finally sold after the war to the Mexican Government.

Richard Kidder Meade served for a year as an army training ship and was then laid up for some time until sunk as a breakwater in 1949.

Willis A. Slater made some trips carrying sulphur, and was then used as an army training ship on the west coast. She, too, was sunk as a breakwater in 1949.

Leonard Chase Wason served in the Pacific until the war ended, and was then laid up and sunk with several others at Kiptopeke.

Fig. 35.—s.s. *Leonard Chase Wason.*

John Smeaton plied in the sugar trade to Cuba. Next she was used as an army storeship in the Pacific. It is known that in 1959 (the last report we have) the Powell River Coy was using her as a floating breakwater, together with several other concrete ships: *Henri Le Chatelier, Thaddeus Merriman, L. J. Vicat* and *Armand Considère*.

The *Joseph Aspdin* began service in May 1944. On one trip she was caught in a terrible hurricane with a wind velocity of 120 miles per hour, and with waves reported to be sixty to eighty feet high. She rolled 20° to starboard and 12° to port and pitched considerably, but there was little vibration and no damage except to her lifeboats. She later became an army storeship in the South Pacific. She was laid up for a while, and then broke away from her moorings to end her days on the North Reef of Yaquina Bay, Oregon, in 1948.

John Grant was documented on June 8, 1944, and traded privately for a while before becoming an army storeship in the South Pacific.

Henri Le Chatelier had basically the same history as *John Grant*, but later finished up as a floating breakwater.

L. J. Vicat also served as an army storeship in the South Pacific.

Robert Whitman Lesley was also used as an army storeship, South Pacific, and ended her time at Kiptopeke as a breakwater.

Edwin Thatcher had a very similar career to the above ship.

C. W. Pasley: she, too, saw service in the South Pacific and was then later sunk as a wharf at Yaquina Bay, Newport.

Armand Considère traded to Japan at the close of the war, and, as already mentioned, was later purchased by the Powell River Coy.

François Hennebique also made trips to Japan and later was sunk at Yaquina Bay, where her superstructure serves as an office for the Yaquina Bay Dock and Dredge Coy.

P. M. Anderson apparently made only one voyage to Manila before being laid up and used as a breakwater.

Albert Kahn, Willard A. Pollard, William Foster Cowham: all three served as army storeships in the South Pacific and the first sailed to Japan in the spring of 1946. All three were later sunk; two as breakwaters, and one after being damaged in a typhoon.

Edwin Clarence Eckel, Thaddeus Merriman, Emile N. Vidal: all saw useful, if short, service at sea.

As well as these ships, the USA built many concrete barges of various kinds.

In conclusion, let us quote from Mrs Haviland's work, *American Concrete Steamers*, her judgment of these vessels.

'There was general agreement that they were entirely seaworthy. and that they handled well. At least three of them passed through hurricanes without appreciable damage. Moreover, it would appear from the reports of several collisions and one or two strandings that they were less fragile than their predecessors of the First World War. A particular merit was that there was no condensation in them as in steel ships, and as a consequence, their cargo kept particularly well. On the debit side was their slow speed. They had been designed for a speed of ten knots and under favourable conditions made as much as $10\frac{1}{2}$ knots. Leaking fuel oil tanks was a frequent cause of complaint, but this is certainly a defect that could have been overcome. One master complained that the crew's quarters were unbearably hot in warm weather, but otherwise he was much pleased with his ship and definitely preferred her to a Liberty ship.'

Some day, in your author's opinion, a breakthrough will almost certainly be made in the construction of large pre-stressed concrete ships, just as has been made in the building of ferro-cement vessels under, say, 100 feet. Concrete as a shipbuilding material still presents an exciting challenge.

Bibliography on concrete ships and ferro-cement

ANON. 'Thin Shell reinforced Concrete in the U.K.'. *Engineering*, Vol. 195, February 8, 1963, p. 232.

ANON. *Vom Caementum Zum Spannbeton* (From Roman concrete to prestressed concrete), published by Bauverlag, G.m.b.H. Wiesbaden.

ANON. 'Glass-cement as a structural material'. *Beton i Zhelezobeton*, June, 1961.

ANON. *Shipbuilding and Shipping Record*, Vols. 12, 1918; 13, 1919.

ANON. 'Une Relique Retrouvée: La Barque de Lambot'. *BATIR*, Oct, 1965.

ANON. U.S. Congress Senate reports, 1918; Concrete Ship Construction. Washington Govt.

AYRE, SIR A. L. 'Merchant Shipbuilding during the War'. *Trans. R.I.N.A.*, Vol. 87, 1945, p. 1 (see p. 10 and discussion by M. P. Payne, E. F. Spanner and N. Wates).

BAKENNUS, R. E. 'Development of Shipyards in the United States during the Great War'. *Trans. S.N.A.M.E.*, Vol. 27, 1919, p. 29.

BYRNE, J. G. and WRIGHT, W. 'Reinforced cement-mortar construction, (Ferro-cement)'. *Concrete and Constructional Engineering*, Vol. 56, No. 12, December, 1961, pp. 429–432.

BYRNE and WRIGHT 'Reinforced Cement Mortar Construction.' *Concrete*, December, 1961.

COLLEN, L. D. G. 'Some Experiments in Design and Construction with Ferro-cement'. *Civil Engineering and Public Works Review*, Vol. 55, No. 643, February, 1960, p. 255.

COLLEN, L. D. G. 'Some Experiments in Design and Construction with Ferro-cement'. *Transactions of the Institution of Civil Engineers of Ireland*, Vol. 86, p. 40.

COLLEN, L. D. G. and KIRWAN, R. W. 'Some Notes on the Characteristics of Ferro-cement'. *Civil Engineering and Public Works Review*, Vol. 54, No. 632, February, 1959, pp. 195–196.

COLLEN, L. D. G. and KIRWAN, R. W. 'The mechanical properties of ferro-cement'. *Civil Engineering and Public Works Review*, December, 1958.

E. M. CROMWELL & CO. 'Epoxy Resin for Consolidating Concrete "Cootmareyne"'. *Eng.*, 13, 11/63.

DENNY, M. 'Preliminary Survey of the possibilities of Reinforced Concrete as a material for Ship Construction.' *Trans. I.N.A.*, Vol. 60, 1918, p. 123.

103

FREYSSINET, E. '*Construction de Coques en Ciment Arme*' (1921). *The Birth of Prestressing*. Prestressed Concrete Ltd, Auckland, New Zealand.

HAVILAND, JEAN 'American Concrete Steamers of the First and Second World Wars'. *Neptune Magazine*, Vol. 22, No. 3, 1962.

ISHAI and BAVLI 'Shrinkage and Cracking of Cement Mortars Used for Exterior Coating'. *Journal of the American Concrete Institute*, November, 1966.

JAMES, R. K. 'U.S. Fleet Maintenance and Battle-Damage Repairs in the Pacific during World War II'. *Trans. N.E.C. Instn. Engineers & Shipbuilders*, Vol. 67, 1950–51, p. 355 (see p. 360).

JAMES, 'Use of concrete' in *Fishing Boats of the World*, 3. United Nations (FAO) publication.

LITTMAN, H. Z. 'Mesh reinforcement for doubly-curved slabs'. *Concrete and Constructional Engineering*, Vol. 55, No. 2, February, 1960, pp. 103–104.

NERVI, P. L. 'Ferro Cement: its Characteristics and Potentialities'. *L'Ingegnere*, 1951. Translated from Italian by the Cement and Concrete Association.

NERVI, P. L. 'Structures'. *Information on Ferro-cement*, F. W. Dodge Corp., 1956.

OWENS, E. G. 'On the Design & Construction of Self-Propelled Reinforced Concrete Sea-going Cargo Steamers, now building in Great Britain'. *Trans. R.I.N.A.*, Vol. 60, p. 154.

PAVRY, R. 'Mulberry Pierheads'. *The Civil Engineer in War*, Vol. 2, p. 369 (see p. 375 and 391) Instn. Civil Engineers, 1948.

PINSTER-WALDER, U. 'Reinforced Concrete Ships of Shell-type Design'. *Z.V.D.I.*, Vol. 91, 1949, p. 157.

POLLOCK, W. 'Reinforced Concrete Vessels'. *Trans. R.I.N.A.*, Vol. 60, 1918, p. 138.

ROMUALDI, J. P. 'The Static Cracking Stress and Fatigue Strength of Concrete Reinforced with Short Pieces of Thin Steel Wire'. Cement and Concrete Association, London.

SCOTT, 'Concrete Shipbuilding in the United States of America'. *Trans. R.I.N.A.*, Vol. 61, 1919, p. 215.

TODD, F. H. 'Some Model Experiments carried out in connection with the Mulberry Harbour'. *Trans. I.N.A.*, Vol. 88, 1946, p. 196.

TICHY, M. 'The application of armocement in the Soviet Union'. *Technical Digest*, Vol. 5, No. 1, January, 1963. pp. 14–20.

VASTA, J. 'The Concrete Ship Programme of World War II'. *Trans. S.N.A.M.E. (Chesapeak Section)*, 1952.

VISHWANATH, T. *et al.* 'Test of a Ferro-Cemento Precast Folded Plate'. *Proceedings of the American Society of Civil Engineers* (Journal of the Structural Division), Vol. 91 (ST6), December, 1965.

WIG, R. J. 'Present Status of the Concrete Ship'. *Trans. S.N.A.M.E.*, Vol. 26, 1918, p. 185.

WIG, R. J. 'Method of Construction of Concrete Ships'. *Trans. S.N.A.M.E.*, Vol. 27, 1919, p. 1.

WILLIAMS, SIR E. O. 'Shear Stresses in Reinforced Concrete with particular reference to Concrete Ships', *J. Instn. Civil Engineers*, No. 7, 1946, p. 377.

WOOD, O. R. J. 'Phoenix'. *The Civil Engineer in War*, Vol. 2, p. 336, Instn. Civil Engineers, 1948.

WOOD, O. R. J. 'Reinforced Concrete Pier Pontoons & Intermediate Pierhead Pontoons'. *The Civil Engineer in War*, Vol. 2, p. 401, Instn. Civil Engineers, 1948.

INDEX